Disclaimer

Published by
CAC Publishing LLC

ISBN: 978-1-948489-48-5 Hardback
ISBN: 978-1-948489-49-2 ebook

Table of Contents

Recipes

Recipes

Recipes

Recipes

Introduction

We all feel the need to eat healthily and with a good reason. A lot has been written and said about making some drastic changes to our everyday diet in order to preserve good health. Modern lifestyles and eating habits, where junk food and sugar are major components, have devastating effects on our bodies. Many different studies have confirmed a strong link between our Western diet and numerous health issues. Over the last century, we have been increasingly exposed to processed and unhealthy ingredients without even knowing it. As such, the decision to change your eating habits can literally be a life or death decision.

Two main factors that greatly contribute to weight gain and poor health are unnatural ingredients and unhealthy preparation methods. Our meals are mostly made from store-bought processed foods loaded with empty calories, bad carbs, saturated and polyunsaturated fats. Good old-fashioned, organic ingredients prepared naturally, like our grandmothers used to do, have been forgotten. Furthermore, our busy schedules are preventing us from leading the good and healthy lives we deserve. So rather than making some small changes in your daily diet, it is better to completely change the way you eat and adopt new habits that will keep your health in check.

The answer lies in the Mediterranean lifestyle. By choosing this lifestyle, you ensure that you don't eat unhealthy ingredients and that you feed your body organic and healthy ingredients prepared in the best possible way – the Mediterranean way! The Mediterranean diet is based on real, old-fashioned foods, lots of proteins, good carbs, and healthy fats. Foods that are traditionally served in this region are loaded with vital vitamins and minerals making them a perfect option for the entire family.

But what is it that makes this diet so special? First, you have to understand that the Mediterranean diet is not some new form of dieting. On the contrary, this is an old-fashioned lifestyle that is typical for this region and includes many different elements. In simple language – a traditional Mediterranean diet is a way of eating and cooking regional foods that have a couple of things in common:

- Locally grown ingredients
- Old-fashioned cooking methods
- A superb taste recognized worldwide

Most nutritionists agree that a proper and well-balanced Mediterranean diet is the world's healthiest diet which provides the body exactly what it needs and in the right amounts. Some might think that preparing these locals meals requires special skills and cooking experience, it doesn't. This diet is a wonderful mix of fresh fruits and vegetables, complex carbs like polenta, potatoes, rice, and pasta; moderate use of dairy products, and regular use of fish and seafood. These amazingly healthy ingredients are usually served with a pure, omega-3 fatty acid-rich olive oil, and then combined into simple recipes that provide all the nutrients your body needs to stay healthy and function properly. The Mediterranean diet is a no brainer – it is a simple yet healthy cooking inherited from our ancestors and perfectly designed for all humans.

Benefits of the Mediterranean Diet

According to the World Health Organization (WHO), health is a state of "complete physical, mental, and social well-being". Health, well-being, and beauty are the most precious gifts you can give to yourself. We all have a tendency to stay healthy and it's a rare gift, especially in modern times where life is packed with different chemicals that destroy our health in so many different ways. In such times, our number one priority in life should be to stay healthy.

As someone who is concerned with healthy living, the chances are you've tried a few diets and nutrition programs yourself. In most cases, you likely didn't see quite the results that you were hoping for while following these diets and now you want something better – something that will finally clean up your body and improve your health once and for all. In order to achieve this, you have to understand one thing:all disease begins in the gut (Hippocrates). Our gastrointestinal system is the system of our digestive organs and one of the most complex microbial ecosystems on Earth. The influence it has on our overall health is enormous – it directly affects our brain, heart, skin, weight, mood, and health in general. Naturally, our gut is tightly related to the foods we eat. In other words, in order for our gastrointestinal tract to function properly and give our body the nutrients it needs, we have to feed it properly. Proper, well-balanced nutrition is the only solution for the healthy organism that will fight off most disease.

However, a proper diet doesn't mean following some sort of branded diet that, in most cases, deprives your body of crucial nutrients and leads to poor health. A healthy and well-balanced diet cannot be achieved by surviving on lettuce and unsweetened juice. On the contrary, healthy eating means making sure you get the balance right, and this balance lies in eating a wide range of foods that are actually good for your digestive tract and your entire system. This is the only way to help your body strengthen its immune system and fight its own way to success. You have to keep in mind that the food you eat seriously impacts you on a critical cellular level that defines your weight and health in general. Adopt the healthy habit of eating the food that will restore the balance to your body by adopting the world's healthiest nutrition plan – the Mediterranean diet. By following these healthy ways of eating, you will finally manage your weight and improve your health. The Mediterranean diet is based on real foods loaded with lean proteins, healthy carbs and fats, vitamins, minerals, and all the amino acids your body needs. And that's not all – the Mediterranean cuisine is recognized as one of the most delicious cuisines in the world! What more do you need?

The Basic Principles of the Mediterranean Diet

The Mediterranean diet is a simple way of cooking and eating specific foods that are typical for this region. However, there are some specific rules that are to be followed in order to adopt this unique and healthy way of eating.

The rich Mediterranean cuisine is based on traditional foods prepared in the countries around the Mediterranean sea – from Spain, France, Balkans, and Italy, all the way to Greece, Turkey, Egypt, and Tunisia. This wonderfully diverse cultural mix has created a beautiful lifestyle and eating habits that are known as the Mediterranean diet. This diet is based on a complete elimination of highly processed foods, moderate amounts of dairy products, and high intake of complex carbs like pasta, rice, potatoes, and polenta, fresh fruits and vegetables that are extremely rich in dietary fiber, vitamins, and minerals. Heavy meat is usually replaced with fish and seafood – a real goldmine of omega-3 fatty acids, while unhealthy fats are replaced with an excessive use of olive oil in almost everything you eat. Countless studies have confirmed a strong relationship between this lifestyle and a long-term weight loss and health improvement. Foods prepared in the Mediterranean way have the ability to prevent heart disease, type 2 diabetes, and reduce the risk of stroke. Accepting this lifestyle means following certain rules and principles that are good for your health and your entire family.

Eat grains – every single day

One good portion of old-fashioned pasta, potatoes, risotto, or bread should be on your daily menu. In the Mediterranean region, grains are traditionally used to prepare different kinds of pasta, purees, and stews. This might come as a surprise because most of the diets out there are against these foods, but actually, there is nothing wrong with one serving of whole wheat pasta with homemade tomato sauce and fresh goat's cheese. It is the unhealthy additives full of chemicals found in store bought ingredients that stop your body from losing fats stored over the years. Replace them with pure olive oil and fresh ripe tomatoes. Accepting the Mediterranean lifestyle doesn't mean giving up the foods you enjoy! On the contrary, this cuisine will open the doors to some entirely new flavors and aromas you never knew existed.

Eating legumes at least two to three times per week

They are healthy, tasty, and make a perfect base for so many different meals. Including legumes into your daily menu shouldn't be a problem.

Your fats should come from olive oil

This is recognized as one of the most important principles of this lifestyle. It is true that you can find lots of different traditional Mediterranean recipes based on butter and some other fats. It is also true that you can enjoy your favorite omelet recipe with butter and a few slices of ham. Nothing is forbidden in the Mediterranean diet as long as it doesn't become your daily routine. However, you have to understand that most of your daily fats will come from olive oil. The reason for this is quite simple – the Mediterranean region is extremely rich in olives and people are used to eating olives and olive oil every single day. The excessive use of olive oil leads to a misconception that the Mediterranean diet is based on unnatural amounts of fats – up to 35%-40%, but you have to keep in mind that we are talking about healthy fats found in fish, nuts, seeds, and olive oil. Not only that, these fats are healthy for your entire body and they are proven to help with weight loss. Furthermore, these healthy fats prevent heart disease, clean your arteries, and even improve the condition of your skin.

Tomatoes

In this region, tomatoes are used almost every day. You will find them in soups, stews, pasta, pizzas, sandwiches, and salads. Tomatoes are extremely healthy. They are an excellent source of vitamin C, vitamin K, copper potassium, manganese, folate, niacin, vitamin B6, vitamin E, and phosphorus. Tomatoes contain generous amounts of vitamin A – in the form of beta-carotene. This should be a good reason to include fresh ripe tomatoes into your diet.

Lots of fresh fruits and vegetables

The importance of eating fresh fruits and vegetables every single day is something we can't argue about, but when we talk about the Mediterranean diet, you have to understand that eating these foods is almost a cult! You can eat them as much as you like without the fear of gaining weight. The only thing you will get is enormous amounts of precious vitamins and minerals that will solve most of your health problems.

Fish and seafood

The Mediterranean diet means a good portion of freshly caught fish or a lovely seafood risotto at least three times per week. Adopting this tasty habit will have some amazing effects on your body. Fish is a great source of protein and healthy fats and definitely a good choice for a delicious lunch or dinner.

Dairy products and milk

These foods will be on your daily menu but in moderate amounts. The Mediterranean region is famous for countless types of cheese and different dairy products. Parmiggiano, Ricotta, goat's milk, Greek yogurt, Feta, Pecorino, Manchego, Mozzarella, Caciocavallo, and other will make a perfect afternoon snack or a tasty addition to your vegetable salad. These authentic Mediterranean delicacies are usually made with goat's, cow's, sheep, or buffalo milk and they're a great source of proteins, vitamins A and D, calcium, and other essential nutrients. For example, just one ounce of Mozzarella cheese will give you about 200 milligrams of calcium – 1/5 of your recommended daily need.

Herbs and spices

Different herbs and spices are what make the Mediterranean cuisine so beautifully diverse! Without them, you simply can't achieve the authentic 'Mediterranean flavor'. Rosemary, oregano, basil, garlic, thyme, parsley, mint, and cumin are all widely used in different recipes.

Enjoy your food

The Mediterranean diet is not only about the types of foods you eat. It is so much more than that. Eat slowly and chew for a long time! That is the soul of the Mediterranean region. Not only will you enjoy every single bite, this beautiful habit will improve your digestion and fill you up with smaller amounts of food. Take your time and start enjoying food like never before! Remember, this is not some diet with a list of foods you should eat or avoid. The Mediterranean diet is a complete lifestyle based on healthy foods, physical activity, fresh air, positive thinking, and relaxation! Traditional meals include lots of people, good food, and smiling – every single day. Enjoy it!

Olive Oil as a Symbol of the Mediterranean Cuisine

As I mentioned earlier, olive oil is one of the most important parts of the Mediterranean cuisine. This liquid gold, with its unique smell and taste, is loaded with antioxidants and healthy fats. Its health benefits are something all doctors and nutritionists agree on. Extra virgin olive oil has the power to protect your heart and blood vessels, clean your digestive tract, and improve the condition of your skin, hair, and nails.

Olives have been considered as a precious gift of nature in many different cultures throughout history. In ancient Greece, they have been a synonym of peace, fertility, power, and wisdom. This 'holy oil' as they used to call it, has been used in ancient medicine to treat a wide range of health problems, but also in different religious rituals. The cultivation of this superb tree is about 7,000 years old and it's deeply rooted in the Mediterranean culture. Even today, 2,000-year-old trees can be found throughout the region.

A natural, homemade olive oil is usually better and more expensive than the regular ones found in the store. This is quite reasonable and to be expected. However, without a proper laboratory test, you can't be sure what you're getting. Even a homemade olive oil is not always the best one to buy – it all depends on the production quality standards. Understanding a couple of things about the process of making the olive oil can be quite useful when buying it. The best olive oil includes high-quality fruits taken directly from the tree. Olive oil made for a commercial production often includes olives from the ground in order to use every single fruit that can be used. This can greatly affect the smell and the taste of your olive oil. Olives that have been standing on the ground for a couple of days lose water which impacts the quality of the oil. The commercial production of extra virgin olive oil includes a centrifuging method and the best quality olives taken directly from the tree. Make sure to ask these questions before buying your oil. However, the homemade production process of making the olive oil is not that complicated. For centuries, people have been making thishealthy oil without any fancy machines and gadgets. The only thing you will need isaccess to fresh olives. This can be a bit tricky because the olive tree is not something you can grow on your balcony over the year. These trees require lots of space and time to give you the fruits for oil, but it's definitely worth the trouble!

Make Your Own Olive Oil

For one bottle of olive oil, you will need:
8-10 lbs ripe olives
Small olive oil press

Preparation

Rinse the olives and remove twigs and leaves, if any. Place them in the oil press and extract the oil into the attached bucket. Transfer to sterilized bottles using a funnel and store in a cool place away from sunlight. That's all it takes to create a beautiful homemade olive oil for the entire family!

Total Daily Nutritional Facts

Calories: 120	Protein: 0g
Dietary Fiber: 0g 0%	Sugars: 0g
Saturated Fat: 2g 10%	Total Carbs: 0g 0%
Total Fat: 14g 18%	Trans Fat: 0g
Cholesterol: 0mg 0%	Sodium: 0mg 0%

Recipes in this
Cookbook - Overview

By now, you understand that the Mediterranean diet is all about eating fresh, healthy, and organic foods. In this book, you will find beautiful recipes prepared in a unique way for the vibrant touch of the Mediterranean cuisine. This diet is so impressively diverse that you can easily follow your current lifestyle but in a healthier and tastier way. Recipes in this book are carefully chosen to remove the chemicals and other unhealthy ingredients found in processed foods and offer you a healthier alternative.

In this book, you will find a 30-day precise diet plan for perfect, long-term weight loss. Unlike other quick-fix diets, you will be allowed to eat all the foods this rich region has to offer, but with one simple limitation – moderate amounts of everything. Your calorie consumption will be limited to 1200-1300 calories per day, which is perfect for safe and healthy weight loss without any side-effects. But the best part of this diet program is the freedom to eat your favorite foods – from pasta, wraps, creamy soups, grill, to desserts like chocolate cake and ice cream! These foods are carefully divided between healthy meals to avoid sudden sugar spikes and help you stay on the path to weight loss.

Following this meal plan will give you the opportunity to try some new ingredients that are typical for this region and to finally understand why the Mediterranean diet wears the title of the healthiest and the tastiest cuisine in the world. The meat will be tender as never before and the vegetables soft and crispy at the same time. And above all – you will finally achieve your perfect body weight!

Try these recipes and follow the Mediterranean diet and you will discover an entirely new dimension to the word 'delicious'. Enjoy!

30 Day Mediterranean Diet Meal Plan

	Breakfast 6 - 9 AM	Snack 11 - 12 AM	Lunch 2 - 3 PM	Snack 4 - 5 PM	Dinner 6 - 7 PM
Day 1	Chia Oatmeal Black Coffee	Green Apple Smoothie	Marinated Salmon Fillet Fresh Lettuce	Spring Salad with Goat's Cheese	Greek Flatbread Vegetable Pizza
Day 2	Boiled Eggs with Steamed Vegetables Homemade Lemonade	Homemade Salmon Spread	Oven Baked Chicken Risotto 6 toasted almonds	Grilled Garlic Leeks	Adana Kebab Herbal Tea
Day 3	Wild Berries Pancakes Black Coffee	Fruit Salad	Orange Marinated Grilled Catfish Fresh Arugula	Alkmene Apple	Beef Patties with Garlic Dip Cucumber
Day 4	Poached Eggs with Leeks Buckwheat Bread	Banana	Baked Trout Fillet Fresh Arugula	Figs	Chicken Fillets Lettuce Spring Onions
Day 5	Acai Bowl Black Coffee	Raspberry Smoothie	Fish Stew	Orange	Cold Cauliflower Salad Toasted Almonds
Day 6	Poached Eggs with Tomato Black Coffee	Walnuts	Chicken Pudding with Artichoke Pear	Orange Juice	Spanish Cold Gazpacho Buckwheat

	Breakfast 6 - 9 AM	Snack 11 - 12 AM	Lunch 2 - 3 PM	Snack 4 - 5 PM	Dinner 6 - 7 PM
Day 7	Homemade Fig Jam Black Coffee	Plums	Marinated Sea Bream Homemade Lemonade	Almond Balls	Spring Salad with Cranberries Buckwheat Bread
Day 8	Blueberry Yogurt with Hazelnuts Herbal Tea	Apple	Pepper Meat Fresh Lettuce Lemon Juice	Hazelnuts	Greek Salad with Fresh Goat's Cheese
Day 9	Panzanella to go Black Coffee	Kiwi	Cold Okra Salad Buckwheat Bread Herbal Tea	Marble Bread	Red Pollock Stew
Day 10	Homemade Fig Jam Black Coffee	Grapefruit Juice	Classic Ragout Soup	Chicken Drumstick Salad	Grilled Eel with Garlic Steamed Spinach
Day 11	Cherry Smoothie Black Coffee	Boiled Potatoes with Spring Onions and Olive Oil	Mediterranean Grilled Shrimps	Toasted Almonds	Thick Lentil Soup
Day 12	Tomato Omelet Whole Grain Bread	Herbal Tea	Anchovy and Mussels Risotto	Greek Yogurt	Tuna Pizza
Day 13	Mediterranean Cream Cheese Whole Grain Bread Black Coffee	Black Coffee	Veal Steak with Mushrooms	Creamy Asparagus Soup	Spinach Pie Plain Yogurt

	Breakfast 6 - 9 AM	Snack 11 - 12 AM	Lunch 2 - 3 PM	Snack 4 - 5 PM	Dinner 6 - 7 PM
Day 14	Boiled Eggs with Spinach and Nuts Black Coffee	Orange	Black Seafood Risotto with Rosemary	Almonds Herbal Tea	Braised Greens with Fresh Mint Greek Yogurt
Day 15	Blueberry Strudel	Black Coffee	Marinated Catfish Fillets	Greek Dolmades	Winter Lamb Stew Lemonade
Day 16	Berry Waffles Herbal Tea	Steamed Spinach	Fresh Goat's Cheese Salad Buckwheat Bread	Creme Caramel	Fish Stew Fresh Lettuce
Day 17	Chocolate Oatmeal with Berries Herbal Tea	Vanilla Pudding	Thick Okra Soup Buckwheat Bread	Kiwi	Grilled Beef Steak Arugula
Day 18	Moroccan Breakfast Salad Orange Juice	Walnuts	Seafood Pasta with Fresh Parsley Fresh Lettuce	Lemonade	Ground Beef Kebab Onion Buckwheat Bread
Day 19	Vanilla French Toast Black Coffee	Figs	Pasta Bolognese Shredded Cabbage	Kefir	Braised Swiss Chard Tomato
Day 20	Goat's Cheese Omelet Black Coffee	Berry Cake	Stuffed Onions Greek Yogurt	Lemonade	Grilled Beef Liver Steamed Spinach

	Breakfast 6 - 9 AM	Snack 11 - 12 AM	Lunch 2 - 3 PM	Snack 4 - 5 PM	Dinner 6 - 7 PM
Day 21	Baked Avocado Eggs Green Tea	Herbal Tea	Braised Green with Beef Lettuce	Cooked Carrots	Collard Greens with Shrimps
Day 22	Spinach Omelet with Kefir Black Coffee	Chocolate Smoothie	Cold Green Bean Salad with Fresh Lime	Red Lentil Soup	Wild Salmon with Spinach
Day 23	Easy Chicken Wraps Black Coffee	Almonds	Mediterranean Scallops Grilled Asparagus Banana	Cooked Cauliflower	Garlic Meatballs
Day 24	Eggs Stuffed with Shrimps Avocado and Spices Lemonade	Herbal Tea	Funghi Pizza	Banana	Orange Baked Whiting Buckwheat Bread
Day 25	Poached Eggs with Garlic and Leeks Black Coffee	Classic Churros with Lemon	Spring Spinach Soup Buckwheat Bread	Herbal tea	Wild Asparagus with Tuna and Garlic
Day 26	Blueberry Greek Yogurt with Bananas Black Coffee	Grapes	Oven Baked Sea Bream Buckwheat Bread	Vegetable Couscous	Italian Seafood Salad with Red Oranges
Day 27	Scrambled Eggs with Cranberries Green Tea	Spinach Triangles	Lemon Baked Chicken Steamed Spinach	Almonds	Braised Greens with Rice

	Breakfast 6 - 9 AM	Snack 11 - 12 AM	Lunch 2 - 3 PM	Snack 4 - 5 PM	Dinner 6 - 7 PM
Day 28	Vanilla Pancakes Black Coffee	Apple	Collard Greens with Veal Lemonade	Avocado Chunks	Tender Octopus Salad Green Tea
Day 29	Mushroom Omelet Green Tea	Coffee Almonds Banana	Vegetable Paella	Strawberry Vanilla Rolls	Sweet Potato and Pumpkin Soup Herbal Tea
Day 30	Overnight Oats with Fruit Green Tea	Lemonade	Lemon Stuffed Tench Fresh Lettuce	Melon	Spanish Paella Herbal Tea

Note:
If you don't like a recipe please feel free to go through the recipes and switch it out for something you would enjoy. If you don't have access to any of the ingredients where you live, like Octopus for example, feel free to substitute your favorite seafood.

Day 1

Breakfast
1 serving Frozen Chia Oatmeal
1 cup black coffee, sugar-free

Snack
1 serving Green Apple Smoothie

Lunch
1 serving Lemon Marinated Salmon Fillet
2 oz fresh lettuce

Snack
1 serving Spring Salad with Goat's Cheese

Dinner
1 serving Greek Flatbread Vegetable Pizza
1 serving Wild Berries Pancakes

Total Daily Nutritional Facts

Calories: 1286	Protein: 69.1g
Carbs: 102g 35%	Fiber: 19.2g 68%
Sugars: 45.6g	Total Fat: 73.2g 94%
Saturated Fat: 23g 114%	Trans Fat: 0g
Cholesterol: 199mg 72%	Sodium: 2411mg 86%

Day 2

Breakfast
1 serving Boiled Eggs with Steamed Vegetables
1 cup homemade lemonade, sugar-free

Snack
1 serving Homemade Salmon Spread

Lunch
1 serving Oven-Baked Chicken Risotto
6 toasted almonds

Snack
1 serving Grilled Garlic Leeks

Dinner
1 serving Adana Kebab
1 cup herbal tea, sugar-free

Total Daily Nutritional Facts

Calories: 1203	Protein: 70.2g
Carbs: 78.9g 27%	Fiber: 11.6g 43%
Sugars: 30.3g	Total Fat: 60g 78.6%
Saturated Fat: 15.2g 76%	Trans Fat: 0g
Cholesterol: 264mg 97%	Sodium: 1961mg 85%

Day 3

Breakfast
1 serving Wild Berries Pancakes
1 cup black coffee, sugar-free

Snack
1 serving Fruit Salad

Lunch
1 serving Orange Marinated Grilled Catfish
2 oz fresh arugula

Snack
1 Alkmene apple

Dinner
1 serving Beef Patties with Garlic Dip
1 small cucumber

Total Daily Nutritional Facts

Calories: 1205	Protein: 68.8g
Carbs: 109.3g 37%	Fiber: 18.5g 67%
Sugars: 60.3g	Total Fat: 59.2g 75%
Saturated Fat: 10.9g 55%	Trans Fat: 0g
Cholesterol: 200mg 73%	Sodium: 1444mg 64%

Day 4

Breakfast
1 serving Poached Eggs with Leeks
1 slice buckwheat bread

Snack
1 banana

Lunch
1 serving Baked Trout Fillet
2 oz fresh arugula

Snack
3 medium-sized figs

Dinner
1 serving Chicken Fillets
2 oz fresh lettuce
2 spring onions

Total Daily Nutritional Facts

Calories: 1177	Protein: 72g
Carbs: 82.1g 41%	Fiber: 13.3g 48%
Sugars: 32.8g	Total Fat: 56.3g 72%
Saturated Fat: 7.3g 36%	Trans Fat: 0g
Cholesterol: 237mg 86%	Sodium: 791mg 35%

Day 5

Breakfast
1 serving Acai Bowl
1 cup coffee, sugar-free

Snack
1 serving Raspberry Smoothie

Lunch
1 serving fish stew
1 serving homemade polenta

Snack
1 orange

Dinner
1 serving Cold Cauliflower Salad
1 oz toasted almonds

Total Daily Nutritional Facts

Calories: 1286	Protein: 64.1g
Carbs: 132.5g 44%	Fiber: 28g 100%
Sugars: 56.9g	Total Fat: 61.2g 79%
Saturated Fat: 9.7g 49%	Trans Fat: 0g
Cholesterol: 98mg 36%	Sodium: 926mg 40%

Day 6

Breakfast
1 serving Poached Eggs with Tomato
1 cup coffee, sugar-free

Snack
2 oz walnuts

Lunch
1 serving Chicken Pudding with Artichoke
1 pear

Snack
1 cup freshly squeezed orange juice

Dinner
1 serving Spanish Cold Gazpacho
1 slice buckwheat bread

Total Daily Nutritional Facts

Calories: 1246	Protein: 60.4g
Carbs: 116.5g 38%	Fiber: 22.7g 81%
Sugars: 56.3g	Total Fat: 65.6g 79%
Saturated Fat: 12.7g 63%	Trans Fat: 0g
Cholesterol: 280mg 102%	Sodium: 1577mg 68%

Day 7

Breakfast
1 serving Fig Jam
1 cup coffee, sugar-free

Snack
2 plums

Lunch
1 serving Marinated Sea Bream
1 cup homemade lemonade

Snack
1 serving Almond Balls

Dinner
1 serving Spring Salad with Cranberries
1 slice buckwheat bread

Total Daily Nutritional Facts

Calories: 1196	Protein: 69.9g
Carbs: 158g 53%	Fiber: 16.7g 59%
Sugars: 112.1g	Total Fat: 32g 40%
Saturated Fat: 7.9g 40%	Trans Fat: 0g
Cholesterol: 64mg 24%	Sodium: 758mg 33%

Week 1
Shopping List

Meat & Fish

- Salmon fillet, 1lb.
- Smoked Salmon, 4 oz.
- Chicken drumsticks, 5 Flathead catfish, 1 lb.
- Ground beef, 1 lb.
- Trout fillets, 2 lbs.
- Ground lamb, 7 oz.
- Ground veal, 7 oz.
- Canned tuna, 2 oz.
- Chicken breast, 1 lb.
- Sea bream, 2 lbs.

Fruits

- Frozen wild berries 10 oz.
- Green apples, 2
- Lemon, 1.8 lb.
- Kiwi, 1Oranges, 10
- Bananas, 1
- Raspberries, 7 oz.
- Frozen strawberries, 5 oz.
- Plums, 2
- Blueberries, 8 oz.
- Cranberries, 10 oz.
- Blackberries, 3.5 oz.
- Pear, 1
- Figs, 2 lbs.

Vegetables & Legumes

- Fresh spinach, 3.5 oz
- Celery stalks, 12 oz
- Cucumbers, 5
- Red onions, 3
- Tomato, 2 lbs
- Spring onions, 8
- Green peas, 2.5 oz
- Red bell peppers, 2
- Green beans, 5 oz
- Fire roasted tomatoes, 12 oz
- Alkmene apple, 1
- Arugula 4 oz
- Garlic, 2 heads
- Lettuce, 6 oz
- Yellow bell pepper, 1
- Onions, 6
- Eggplant, 1
- Carrots, 4
- Artichokes, 2
- Broccoli, 1 lb
- Cauliflower, 1 lb
- Leeks, 5

Dairy Products & Eggs

- Goat's milk, 8 fl oz.
- Skim milk, 1-quart
- Fresh goat's cheese, 10 oz.
- Sour cream 8 fl oz.
- Butter 3.5 oz.
- Cream cheese 3.5 oz.
- Mozzarella, 3.5 oz.
- Greek yogurt, 19 oz.

Nuts & Seeds

- Chia seeds, 1 small pack
- Sesame seeds, 1 small pack
- Walnuts, 2 oz.
- Almonds, 1lb
- Cumin seeds, 2 oz.

Herbs & Spices

- Oregano, 1 small pack
- Vanilla sugar, 1 small pack
- Parsley, 7 oz.
- Cayenne pepper, 1 small pack
- Black pepper, 1 small pack
- Dried thyme, 1 small pack
- Dried basil, 1 small pack
- Pink Himalayan salt
- Cumin powder, 1 small pack
- Strawberry extract
- Vanilla extract
- Red pepper flakes, 1 small pack
- Italian seasoning, 1 small pack
- Sumac, 1 small pack
- Coriander powder, 1 small pack
- Dried rosemary, 1 small pack
- Mustard seeds, 1 small pack
- Dill sprigs, 1 small pack
- Garlic powder, 1 small pack
- Brown sugar, ½ cup

Other

- Rolled oats, 10 oz
- Honey, 2 fl oz
- Extra virgin olive oil, 1 bottle
- Olives, 1 small jar
- Buckwheat flour, 7 oz
- Dark chocolate, 7 oz
- Buckwheat bread, 1 pack
- Apple cider, 1 small bottle
- Stevia powder, 1 small pack
- Brown rice, 7 oz
- Cocoa powder, 3.5 oz
- All-purpose flour, 3.5 oz
- Dijon mustard, 1 small pack
- Flatbread dough, 7 oz
- Tomato pizza sauce, 1 small jar
- Corn flour, 1 lb
- Tomato paste, 1 small jar
- Acai powder, 3.5 oz
- Herbal tea
- Whole grain bread, 1 pack
- Brown sugar, ½ cup
- Ground cinnamon, 1 tsp.

Day 8

Breakfast
1 serving Blueberry Yogurt with Hazelnuts
1 cup herbal tea, sugar-free

Snack
1 apple

Lunch
1 serving Pepper Meat
1 oz fresh lettuce
1 cup freshly squeezed lemon juice, sugar-free

Snack
1 oz hazelnuts

Dinner
1 serving Greek Salad with Fresh Goat's Cheese

Total Daily Nutritional Facts

Calories: 1262	Protein: 77.4g
Carbs: 94.1g 31%	Fiber: 17.4g 62%
Sugars: 66.6g	Total Fat: 67.5g 86%
Saturated Fat: 20.7g 103%	Trans Fat: 0g
Cholesterol: 209mg 76%	Sodium: 1132mg 49%

Day 9

Breakfast
1 serving Panzanella to go
1 cup black coffee, sugar-free

Snack
1 kiwi

Lunch
1 serving Cold Okra Salad
1 slice buckwheat bread
1 cup herbal tea, sugar-free

Snack
1 serving Marble Bread

Dinner
1 serving Red Pollock Stew

Total Daily Nutritional Facts

Calories: 1283	Protein: 53.2g
Carbs: 151.3g 50%	Fiber: 24.5g 86%
Sugars: 62.2g	Total Fat: 58.6g 75%
Saturated Fat: 9.3g 46%	Trans Fat: 0g
Cholesterol: 50mg 19%	Sodium: 1276mg 55%

Day 10

Breakfast
1 serving Homemade Fig Jam
1 Wasa cracker
1 cup black coffee, sugar-free

Snack
1 cup freshly squeezed grapefruit juice

Lunch
1 serving Classic Ragout Soup

Snack
1 serving Chicken Drumstick Salad

Dinner
1 serving Grilled Eel with Garlic
1 cup steamed spinach

Total Daily Nutritional Facts

Calories: 1288	Protein: 61.1g
Carbs: 106.9g 36%	Fiber: 19.4g 68%
Sugars: 61.7g	Total Fat: 66.4g 86%
Saturated Fat: 11.9g 58.3%	Trans Fat: 0g
Cholesterol: 211mg 77%	Sodium: 1797mg 78%

Day 11

Breakfast
1 serving Cherry Smoothie
1 cup black coffee, sugar-free

Snack
1 serving Boiled Potatoes with Spring Onions and Olive Oil

Lunch
1 serving Mediterranean Grilled Shrimps

Snack
4 toasted almonds

Dinner
1 serving Thick Lentil Soup
1 slice buckwheat bread

Total Daily Nutritional Facts

Calories: 1224	Protein: 56.8g
Carbs: 132g 44%	Fiber: 18.6g 57%
Sugars: 25.3g	Total Fat: 54.1g 69%
Saturated Fat: 11g 55%	Trans Fat: 0g
Cholesterol: 206mg 65%	Sodium: 2646mg 116%

Day 12

Breakfast
1 serving Tomato Omelet
1 slice whole grain bread

Snack
1 cup herbal tea

Lunch
1 serving Anchovy and Mussels Risotto

Snack
½ cup Greek yogurt

Dinner
1 serving Tuna Pizza

Total Daily Nutritional Facts

Calories: 1263	Protein: 56g,
Carbs: 116.8g 39%	Fiber: 7.1g 26%
Sugars: 19.5g,	Total Fat: 61.8g 80%
Saturated Fat: 19.6g 97%	Trans Fat: 0g
Cholesterol: 213mg 78%	Sodium: 1924mg 83%

Day 13

Breakfast
1 serving Mediterranean Cream Cheese
1 slice whole grain bread

Snack
1 cup black coffee, sugar-free

Lunch
1 serving Veal Steak with Mushrooms

Snack
1 serving Creamy Asparagus Soup

Dinner
1 serving Spinach Pie
½ cup plain yogurt, fat-free

Total Daily Nutritional Facts

Calories: 1291	Protein: 71.6g
Carbs: 58.1g 19%	Fiber: 10.3g 36%
Sugars: 22.2g	Total Fat: 88.2g 112%
Saturated Fat: 39.5g 196%	Trans Fat: 0g
Cholesterol: 374mg 137%	Sodium: 2690mg 116%

Day 14

Breakfast
1 serving Boiled Eggs with Spinach and Nuts
1 cup black coffee, sugar-free

Snack
1 orange

Lunch
1 serving Black Seafood Risotto with Rosemary

Snack
5 almonds
1 cup herbal tea, sugar-free

Dinner
1 serving Braised Greens with Fresh Mint
1 cup Greek yogurt

Total Daily Nutritional Facts

Calories: 1272	Protein: 66.5g
Carbs: 118g 39%	Fiber: 46.2g 74%
Sugars: 31.5g	Total Fat: 63.6g 82%
Saturated Fat: 12.7g 63%	Trans Fat: 0g
Cholesterol: 290mg 106%	Sodium: 2240mg 97%

Week 2
Shopping List

Meat & Fish

- Beef fillet, 2 lbs
- Pollock fillet, 1 lb
- Lamb Chops, 1 lb
- Chicken drumsticks, 4
- Eel, 1 lb
- Shrimps, 1 lb
- Bacon, 7 oz
- Mussels, 7 oz
- Anchovies salted, 4
- Oil-free tuna, 1 can
- Veal steak, 1 lb
- Seafood mix, 1 lb

Fruits

- Blueberries, 1.5 oz
- Figs, 2 lbs
- Apple, 1
- Lemons, 6
- Kiwi, 1 piece
- Grapefruit, 2
- Cherries, 5 oz

Vegetables & Legumes

- Onions, 2 lbs
- Lettuce, 5 oz
- Red cabbage, 3.5 oz
- Tomato, 2 lbs
- Cucumbers, 3

- Onions, 2 lbs
- Lettuce, 5 oz
- Red cabbage, 3.5 oz
- Tomato, 2 lbs
- Cucumbers, 3
- Red bell pepper, 1 piece
- Garlic, 2 heads
- Okra, 7 oz
- Bean sprouts, 7 oz
- Green peas, 8 oz
- Carrots, 8
- Cherry tomatoes, 14 oz
- Baby corn, 3.5 oz
- Potatos, 4
- Button mushrooms, 1.5 lb
- Spinach, 2 lbs
- Brown lentils, 5 oz
- Arugula, 7 oz
- Swiss chard, 7 oz
- Chicory, 1 lb
- Wild asparagus, 2 lbs
- Celery stalks, 2

Dairy Products & Eggs

- Plain yogurt, 3.5 oz
- Skim milk
- 1-quart gal. ct.
- Fresh goat's cheese, 1.6 lb
- Mozzarella, 5 oz
- Greek yogurt, 20 oz
- Cream cheese, 8 oz
- Mascarpone, 4 oz
- Butter 7 oz
- Eggs, 12
- Heavy Cream, 10 oz
- Feta Cheese, 4 oz

Nuts & Seeds

- Hazelnuts, 2 oz
- Almonds, 14
- Walnuts, 5

Herbs & Spices

- Cinnamon, 1 small pack
- Parsley, 7 oz
- Dijon mustard, 1 small pack
- Italian seasoning, 1 small pack
- Bay leaves, 1 small pack
- Rosemary, 1 small pack
- Cayenne pepper, 1 small pack
- Pink Himalayan salt, 1 small pack
- Dried thyme, 1 small pack
- Cilantro, 7 oz
- Chili pepper, 1 small pack
- Chili flakes, 1 small pack
- Cumin powder, 1 small pack
- Fresh mint, 3-5 oz

Other

- Blueberry extract, 1 small pack
- Honey, 2 fl oz
- Tomato paste, 1 small pack
- Olives, 1 small jar
- Whole grain bread, 1 piece
- Apple cider, 1 small bottle
- White wine, 1 bottle
- Buckwheat bread, 1 piece
- All-purpose flour, 5 oz
- Baking powder, 1 small pack
- Blueberry extract, 1 small pack
- Honey, 2 fl oz
- Tomato paste, 1 small pack
- Olives, 1 small jar
- Whole grain bread, 1 piece
- Apple cider, 1 small bottle
- White wine, 1 bottle
- Buckwheat bread, 1 piece
- All-purpose flour, 5 oz
- Baking powder, 1 small pack
- Stevia, 3.5 oz
- Cherry extract, 1 small pack
- Cocoa powder, 1 oz
- Brown sugar, 4.5 oz
- Wasa crackers, 1 pack
- Calamata olives, 1 small jar
- Coconut water, 8 fl oz
- Rice, 1 lb
- Capers, 1 small jar
- Pizza crust, 7 oz
- Yufka dough, 1 pack
- Calamari ink, 1 small pack

Day 15

Breakfast
1 serving Blueberry Strudel

Snack
1 cup black coffee, sugar-free

Lunch
1 serving Marinated Catfish Fillets

Snack
1 serving Greek Dolmades

Dinner
1 serving Winter Lamb Stew
1 cup lemonade, sugar-free

Total Daily Nutritional Facts

Calories: 1262	Protein: 70g
Carbs: 77.7g 25%	Fiber: 9.9g 35%
Sugars: 15.7g	Total Fat: 63g 80%
Saturated Fat: 14g 70%	Trans Fat: 0g
Cholesterol: 180mg 66%	Sodium: 1071mg 45%

Day 16

Breakfast
1 serving Berry Waffles
1 cup herbal tea, sugar-free

Snack
1 oz steamed spinach

Lunch
1 serving Fresh Goat's Cheese Salad
1 slice buckwheat bread

Snack
1 serving Creme Caramel

Dinner
1 serving Fish Stew
2 oz fresh lettuce

Total Daily Nutritional Facts

Calories: 1282	Protein: 73.4g,
Carbs: 128.4g 43%	Fiber: 9.2g 33%
Sugars: 49.1g	Total Fat: 52.4g 62%
Saturated Fat: 21.6g 109%	Trans Fat: 0g
Cholesterol: 479mg 174%	Sodium: 1503mg 67%

Day 17

Breakfast
1 serving Chocolate Oatmeal with Berries
1 cup herbal tea, sugar-free

Snack
1 serving Vanilla Pudding

Lunch
1 serving Thick Okra Soup
1 slice buckwheat bread

Snack
1 kiwi

Dinner
1 serving Grilled Beef Steak
2 oz arugula

Total Daily Nutritional Facts

Calories: 1218	Protein: 74.2g
Carbs: 117.5g 39%	Fiber: 26.9g 97%
Sugars: 33.3g	Total Fat: 52.7g 44%
Saturated Fat: 6.5g 32%	Trans Fat: 0g
Cholesterol: 427mg 155%	Sodium: 1994mg 87%

Day 18

Breakfast
1 serving Moroccan Breakfast Salad
1 cup freshly squeezed orange juice, sugar-free

Snack
1 oz walnuts

Lunch
1 serving Seafood Pasta with Fresh Parsley
2 oz fresh lettuce

Snack
1 cup lemonade, sugar-free

Dinner
1 serving Ground Beef Kebab
1 small onion
1 slice buckwheat bread

Total Daily Nutritional Facts

Calories: 1262	Protein: 69.1g
Carbs: 160g 53%	Fiber: 18.4g 65%
Sugars: 56.4g	Total Fat: 41.5g 53%
Saturated Fat: 6.2g 25%	Trans Fat: 0g
Cholesterol: 135mg 49%	Sodium: 1574mg 68%

Day 19

Breakfast
1 serving Vanilla French Toast
1 cup black coffee, sugar-free

Snack
2 figs

Lunch
1 serving Pasta Bolognese
2 oz shredded cabbage

Snack
1 cup kefir

Dinner
1 serving Braised Swiss Chard
1 tomato

Total Daily Nutritional Facts

Calories: 1220	Protein: 45.6g
Carbs: 152.9g 50%	Fiber: 23g 82%
Sugars: 49.5g	Total Fat: 49.9g 63%
Saturated Fat: 15.4g 76%	Trans Fat: 0g
Cholesterol: 170mg 62%	Sodium: 1729mg 75%

Day 20

Breakfast
1 serving Goat's Cheese Omelet
1 cup black coffee, sugar-free

Snack
1 serving Berry Cake

Lunch
1 serving Stuffed Onions
2 oz Greek yogurt

Snack
1 cup lemonade, sugar-free

Dinner
1 serving Grilled Beef Liver
1 oz steamed spinach

Total Daily Nutritional Facts

Calories: 1194	Protein: 71g
Carbs: 88.6g 29%	Fiber: 5.9g 22%
Sugars: 40.5g	Total Fat: 62.7g 81%
Saturated Fat: 19.4g 97%	Trans Fat: 0g
Cholesterol: 767mg 297%	Sodium: 2057mg 89%

Day 21

Breakfast
1 serving Baked Avocado Eggs
1 cup green tea, sugar-free

Snack
2 carrots, cooked

Lunch
1 serving Braised Leeks with Beef
2 oz lettuce

Snack
1 cup herbal tea, sugar-free

Dinner
1 serving Collard Greens with Shrimps
1 cup herbal tea, sugar-free

Total Daily Nutritional Facts

Calories: 1218	Protein: 100.4g
Carbs: 65.1g 22%	Fiber: 22g 78%
Sugars: 16.5g	Total Fat: 64.3g 82%
Saturated Fat: 13.4g 67%	Trans Fat: 0g
Cholesterol: 511mg 185%	Sodium: 1940mg 84%

Week 3
Shopping List

Meat & Fish

- Catfish fillets, 1 lb
- Lamb neck, 1 lb
- Shrimp, 2 lbs
- Red Mullet, 1 lb
- Mackerel, 1 piece
- Tench fillets, 1 lb
- Flat iron steak, 1 lb
- Frozen seafood mix, 7 oz
- Ground beef, 2 lbs 7 oz
- Beef liver, 1 lb
- Beef stew meat, 1 lb
- Octopus, 1 lb

Fruits

- Blueberries, 8 oz
- Raspberries, 10 oz
- Lemons, 7
- Blackberries, 3 oz
- Cranberries, 1.5 oz
- Pineapple, 1
- Kiwis, 2
- Pear, 1
- Lime, 1
- Oranges, 2
- Figs, 2
- Avocado, 1

Vegetables & Legumes

- Garlic, 2 head
- Onions, 4 lbs
- Potatos, 4
- Carrots, 7
- Tomato, 2 lbs
- Red bell peppers, 2
- Spinach, 2 oz
- Green bell peppers, 2
- Lettuce, 4 oz
- Celery stalks, 2
- Okra, 1 lb
- Eggplant, 1
- Cabbage, 7 oz
- Arugula, 2 oz
- Cherry tomatoes, 5
- Swiss chard, 1 lb
- Leeks, 6
- Collard greens, 2 lbs

Dairy Products & Eggs

- Greek yogurt, 13 oz
- Eggs, 17
- Butter, 7 lb
- Skim milk, 1 qt. gal.
- Goat's cheese, 10 oz
- Whipping cream, 5 oz
- Heavy cream, 4 oz
- Kefir, 8 fl oz

Nuts & Seeds

- Chia seeds, 1 small pack
- Almonds, 10
- Peanuts, 3.5 oz
- Walnuts, 1 oz

Herbs & Spices

- Salt - Parsley, 7 oz
- Fresh dill, 3.5 oz
- Fresh rosemary, 1 small pack
- Fresh mint, 1 small pack
- Italian seasoning, 1 small pack
- Dried rosemary, 1 small pack
- Cayenne pepper, 1 small pack
- Thyme, 1 small pack
- Bay leaves, 1 small pack
- Red pepper flakes, 1 small pack
- Sea salt
- Dried oregano, 1 small pack
- Black pepper, 1 small pack
- Cinnamon, 1 small pack
- Garlic powder, 1 small pack
- Turmeric, 1 small pack
- Dried mint, 1 small pack
- Cumin powder, 1 small pack
- Celery leaves, 7 oz

Other

- Blueberry extract, 1 small pack
- Stevia powder, 1 small pack
- Cornstarch
- Puff pastry, 2 sheets
- Wine leaves, 40 (typically 1 jar)
- White wine, 1 bottle
- Mustard, 1 small pack
- Olive oil, 1 bottle
- Long grain rice, 7 oz
- All-purpose flour, 2 lbs
- Buckwheat flour, 1 lb
- Vanilla extract, 3 packs
- Coconut oil, 5 oz
- Blueberry jam, 7 oz
- Buckwheat bread, 1 piece
- Brown sugar, 2 lbs
- Rolled oats, 5 oz
- Cocoa powder, 7 oz
- Honey, 1 small jar
- Pasta linguine, 14 oz
- Bicarbonate of soda, 1 small pack
- Whole grain toast bread, 1 piece
- Penne Rigatte, 14 oz
- Tomato paste, 1 small jar
- Baking powder, 1 small pack
- Brown rice, 7 oz
- Italian style breadcrumbs, 3.5 oz

Day 22

Breakfast
1 serving Spinach Omelet with Kefir
1 cup black coffee, sugar-free

Snack
1 serving Chocolate Smoothie

Lunch
1 serving Cold Green Bean Salad with Fresh Lime

Snack
1 serving Red Lentil Soup

Dinner
1 serving Wild Salmon with Spinach

Total Daily Nutritional Facts

Calories: 1269	Protein: 73.7g
Carbs: 86.6g 28%	Fiber: 52.9g 118%
Sugars: 26.3g	Total Fat: 74.5g 95%
Saturated Fat: 15.9g 79%	Trans Fat: 0g
Cholesterol: 190mg 70%	Sodium: 2417mg 105%

Day 23

Breakfast
1 serving Easy Chicken Wraps
1 cup black coffee, sugar-free

Snack
5 almonds

Lunch
1 serving Mediterranean Scallops
7 oz grilled asparagus
1 medium-sized banana

Snack
1 cup cooked cauliflower

Dinner
1 serving Garlic Meatballs

Total Daily Nutritional Facts

Calories: 1264	Protein: 65.5g
Carbs: 137.4g 46%	Fiber: 22.4g 81%
Sugars: 31.7g	Total Fat: 45.3g 58%
Saturated Fat: 7.8g 39%	Trans Fat: 0g
Cholesterol: 143mg 52%	Sodium: 2046mg 89%

Day 24

Breakfast
1 serving Eggs Stuffed with Shrimps Avocado and Spices
1 cup lemonade, sugar-free

Snack
1 banana

Lunch
1 serving Funghi Pizza

Snack
1 cup herbal tea

Dinner
1 serving Orange Baked Whiting
1 slice buckwheat bread

Total Daily Nutritional Facts

Calories: 1209	Protein: 81.8g
Carbs: 122.5g 37%	Fiber: 54.3g 51%
Sugars: 33.5g	Total Fat: 43g 56%
Saturated Fat: 8.7g 43%	Trans Fat: 0g
Cholesterol: 444g 162%	Sodium: 1162mg 49%

Day 25

Breakfast
1 serving Poached Eggs with Garlic and Leeks
1 cup black coffee, sugar-free

Snack
1 serving Classic Churros with Lemon

Lunch
1 serving Spring Spinach Soup
1 slice buckwheat bread

Snack
1 cup herbal tea

Dinner
1 serving Wild Asparagus with Tuna and Garlic

Total Daily Nutritional Facts

Calories: 1180	Protein: 70g
Carbs: 85.4g 29%	Fiber: 12.4g 44%
Sugars: 18.6g	Total Fat: 64.2g 82%
Saturated Fat: 19.6g 97%	Trans Fat: 0g
Cholesterol: 425mg 193%	Sodium: 1700mg 74%

Day 26

Breakfast
1 serving Blueberry Greek Yogurt with Bananas
1 cup black coffee, sugar-free

Snack
1 cup herbal tea

Lunch
1 serving Oven Baked Sea Bream
1 cup homemade lemonade

Snack
1 cup Vegetable Couscous

Dinner
1 serving Italian Seafood Salad with Red Oranges

Total Daily Nutritional Facts

Calories: 1282	Protein: 72.4g
Carbs: 99.2g 32%	Fiber: 15.5g 54%
Sugars: 25.7g	Total Fat: 68.8g 63%
Saturated Fat: 10.5g 54%	Trans Fat: 0g
Cholesterol: 113g 42%	Sodium: 892mg 138%

Day 27

Breakfast
1 serving Scrambled Eggs with Cranberries
1 cup green tea, sugar-free

Snack
1 serving Spinach Triangles

Lunch
1 serving Lemon Baked Chicken
1 cup steamed spinach

Snack
8 almonds

Dinner
1 serving Braised Greens with Rice

Total Daily Nutritional Facts

Calories: 1196	Protein: 78.6g
Carbs: 69g 22%	Fiber: 6.7g 25%
Sugars: 10g	Total Fat: 68.3g 87%
Saturated Fat: 38.1g 91%	Trans Fat: 0g
Cholesterol: 471mg 180%	Sodium: 1405mg 61%

Day 28

Breakfast
1 serving Vanilla Pancakes
1 cup black coffee, sugar-free

Snack
1 medium-sized apple

Lunch
1 serving Collard Greens with Veal
1 cup homemade lemonade

Snack
½ cup avocado chunks

Dinner
1 serving Tender Octopus Salad
1 cup green tea

Total Daily Nutritional Facts

Calories: 1237	Protein: 88.7g
Carbs: 106.6g 37%	Fiber: 24.2g 87%
Sugars: 39.1g	Total Fat: 55g 71%
Saturated Fat: 12.5g 62%	Trans Fat: 0g
Cholesterol: 326mg 119%	Sodium: 1857mg 81%

Day 29

Breakfast
1 serving Mushroom Omelet
1 cup green tea, sugar-free

Snack
1 cup coffee, sugar-free
3 almonds, toasted

Lunch
1 serving Vegetable Paella
1 medium-sized banana

Snack
1 serving Strawberry Vanilla Rolls

Dinner
1 serving Sweet Potato and Pumpkin Soup
1 cup herbal tea, sugar-free

Total Daily Nutritional Facts

Calories: 1205	Protein: 41.4g
Carbs: 167.3g 56%	Fiber: 21.4g 77%
Sugars: 56.5g	Total Fat: 43.9g 56%
Saturated Fat: 16.1g 64%	Trans Fat: 0g
Cholesterol: 260mg 95%	Sodium: 2544mg 96%

Day 30

Breakfast
1 serving Overnight Oats with Fruit
1 cup green tea, sugar-free

Snack
4 dates
5 almonds

Lunch
1 serving Lemon Stuffed Tench
1 slice buckwheat bread
2 oz fresh lettuce

Snack
7 oz melon

Dinner
1 serving Spanish Paella
1 pear
1 cup herbal tea

Total Daily Nutritional Facts

Calories: 1243	Protein: 78.2g
Carbs: 137.6g 45%	Fiber: 20.8g 74%
Sugars: 75.8g	Total Fat: 45.4g 58%
Saturated Fat: 11g 56%	Trans Fat: 0g
Cholesterol: 130mg 47%	Sodium: 1037mg 45%

Week 4
Shopping List

Meat & Fish

- Wild salmon, 1 lb
- Chicken breast, 14 oz
- Mediterranean scallops, 4
- Lean ground beef, 1lb
- Shrimp, 4
- Whiting, 2 lbs
- Lamb rack, 1 lb
- Oil-free tuna, 1 can
- Sea bream, 2 lbs
- Frozen seafood mix, 7 oz
- Whole chicken, 3 lbs
- Veal brisket, 1 lb
- Octopus, 2 lbs
- Tench, 1 medium-sized piece
- Boneless chicken thighs, 1 lb

Fruits

- Lime, 1 piece
- Lemon, 2 lbs
- Bananas, 7
- Avocados, 2
- Oranges, 2
- Cranberries, 3.5 oz
- Apple, 1
- Strawberries, 6 oz
- Blueberries, 3 oz
- Dates, 4
- Melon, 7 oz
- Pear, 1

Vegetables & Legumes

- Spinach, 3 lbs
- Green beans, 1 lb
- Garlic, 2 heads
- Red lentils, 7 oz
- Onions, 2 lbs
- Cucumbers, 2
- Asparagus, 7 oz
- Cauliflower, 5 oz
- Potato, 1 piece
- Button mushrooms, 10 oz
- Leeks, 2 lbs
- Swiss chard, 3 oz
- Wild asparagus, 10 oz
- Lettuce, 3.5 oz
- Red bell pepper, 1 piece
- Swiss chard, 1 lb
- Kale, 4 oz
- Collard greens, 2 lbs
- Celery stalks, 5
- Carrots, 6
- Green peas, 2.5 oz
- Fire roasted tomatoes, 7 oz
- Zucchini, 1
- Celery root, 1
- Pumpkin, 2 lbs
- Sweet potatos, 3
- Artichokes, 2

Nuts & Seeds

- Almonds, 24
- Chia seeds, 2 oz
- Walnuts 4

Dairy Products & Eggs

- Eggs, 24
- Ricotta, 3.5 oz
- Skim milk, half gal.
- Greek yogurt, 10 oz
- Gouda cheese, 2 oz
- Goat's cheese, 11 oz
- Goat's milk, 10 oz
- Kefir, 8 fl oz
- Heavy cream, 2 oz
- Plain yogurt, 4 oz
- Butter, 7 oz

Herbs & Spices

- Salt
- Parsley, 7 oz
- Fresh dill, 3.5 oz
- Fresh rosemary, 1 small pack
- Fresh mint, 1 small pack
- Italian seasoning, 1 small pack
- Dried rosemary, 1 small pack
- Cayenne pepper, 1 small pack
- Thyme, 1 small pack
- Bay leaves, 1 small pack
- Red pepper flakes, 1 small pack
- Sea salt
- Dried oregano, 1 small pack
- Black pepper, 1 small pack
- Cinnamon, 1 small pack
- Garlic powder, 1 small pack
- Turmeric, 1 small pack
- Dried mint, 1 small pack
- Cumin powder, 1 small pack
- Celery leaves, 7 oz

Other

- Olive oil, 1 bottle
- Coconut water, 4 oz
- Cocoa powder, 5 oz
- Vanilla extract, 1 small pack
- Stevia extract, 1 small pack
- Mustard, 1 small pack
- Sweet carrot puree, 1 small jar
- All-purpose flour, 10 oz
- Whole wheat tortillas, 4
- White wine, 1 bottle
- Rice, 1 lb
- Tomato paste, 1 small pack
- Whole wheat flour, 7 oz
- Dried yeast, 2 oz
- Buckwheat bread, 1 piece
- Brown sugar, 3.5 oz
- Coconut oil, 4 oz
- Lemon extract, 1 small pack
- Blueberry extract, 1 small pack
- Couscous, 7 oz
- Frozen filo pastry, 2 sheets
- Honey, 1 small jar
- Brown rice, 8 oz
- Rolled oats, 7 oz
- Baking powder, 1 small pack
- Capers, 1 small jar
- Olives, 1 small jar
- Puff pastry sheets, 2
- Cornstarch, 2 oz
- Vanilla pudding powder, 3 oz
- Strawberry extract, 1 small pack
- Blueberry extract, 1 small pack

Chia Oatmeal

Serves	Preparation Time
2 Persons	**15 min**

Ingredients

½ cup goat's milk
2 tbsp chia seeds
¼ cup rolled oats
1 cup fresh wild berries
1 tsp pure vanilla extract, organic

Preparation

In a medium-sized serving glass, combine goat's milk with chia seeds and vanilla extract. Stir well and let it stand for ten minutes, allowing the seeds to soak in the liquid. Freeze for at least 20 minutes (or even better, freeze overnight).

Remove from the freezer and add rolled oats. Top with wild berries and serve.

Total Daily Nutritional Facts

Calories: 186	Protein: 7.1g	Total Fat: 8.5g 11%	Cholesterol: 7mg 2%
Dietary Fiber: 7.8g 28%	Sugars: 10.3g	Trans Fat: 0g	Sodium: 32mg 1%
Saturated Fat: 2.1g 11%	Total Carbs: 26.4g 9%		

Green Apple Smoothie

Serves   Preparation Time

4 Persons   **10 min**

Ingredients

2 medium-sized green delicious apples
2 cups spinach, finely chopped
1 tbsp freshly squeezed lemon juice
3 celery stalks, chopped
1 large cucumber, peeled and sliced
1 tbsp honey
1 tbsp sesame seeds
1 cup skim milk
2 cups water

Preparation

Combine the ingredients in a blender and pulse until completely smooth.

Serve cold.

Total Daily Nutritional Facts

Calories: 186	Protein: 7.1g	Total Fat: 8.5g 11%	Trans Fat: 0g
Dietary Fiber: 7.8g 28%	Sugars: 10.3g	Cholesterol: 7mg 2%	Sodium: 32mg 1%
Saturated Fat: 2.1g 11%	Total Carbs: 26.4g 9%		

Marinated Salmon Fillet

Serves

2 Persons

Preparation Time

15 min

Cooking Time

25 min

Ingredients

1 lb fresh salmon fillets, skin on
¼ cup extra virgin olive oil
½ cup freshly squeezed lemon juice
2 garlic cloves, crushed
1 tbsp fresh oregano leaves, finely chopped
1 tsp sea salt
¼ tsp red pepper flakes

Preparation

Rinse the fillet well under cold running water and pat dry with kitchen paper. Set aside.
In a small bowl, combine olive oil with lemon juice, crushed garlic, fresh oregano leaves, salt, and red pepper flakes. Generously brush the mixture over the fillet and refrigerate for 20-30 minutes.
Preheat a large, non–stick grill pan over medium-high heat. Remove the fillet from the refrigerator and pat dry to soak up the excess fat.
Grill for 12-15 minutes on one side, or until completely set. Turn once and continue to grill for 10 more minutes.
Serve immediately.

Total Daily Nutritional Facts

Calories: 271	Protein: 22.5g	Total Fat: 20g 26%	Trans Fat: 0g
Dietary Fiber: 0.7g 2%	Sugars: 0.7g	Cholesterol: 50mg 18%	Sodium: 525mg 3%
Saturated Fat: 3.1g 15%	Total Carbs: 1.9g 1%		

Spring Salad with Goat's Cheese

Serves
6 Persons

Preparation Time
20 min

Cooking Time
12 min

Ingredients

2 oz lettuce, torn
2 eggs, hard-boiled and sliced
1 yellow bell pepper, seeds removed and sliced
1 red onion, sliced
1 medium-sized tomato, roughly chopped
1 medium-sized cucumber
3 spring onions, chopped
1 cup fresh goat's cheese
4 tbsp olive oil
2 tbsp freshly squeezed lemon juice
1 tbsp Dijon mustard
1 tsp sugar
2 tbsp freshly grated lemon zest
½ tsp sea salt

Preparation

In a small bowl, combine olive oil with lemon juice, mustard, sugar, lemon zest, and salt. Stir well and refrigerate for 15 minutes. Now gently place the eggs in a deep pot and pour enough cold water to cover. Bring it to a boil and cook for 12 minutes.

Remove from the heat and drain. Rinse under cold water to cool. Peel the eggs and slice them. Place in a deep bowl. Rinse and drain the vegetables. Slice and place into a bowl. Toss well to combine and drizzle with lemon dressing.

Serve immediately.

Total Daily Nutritional Facts

Calories: 274	Protein: 11.3g	Total Fat: 22.4g 29%	Trans Fat: 0g
Dietary Fiber: 1.7g 6%	Sugars: 5.4g	Cholesterol: 84mg 31%	Sodium: 406mg 18%
Saturated Fat: 9.7g 48%	Total Carbs: 9.1g 3%		

Greek Flatbread Vegetable Pizza

Serves	Preparation Time	Cooking Time
4 Persons	15 min	12-15 min

Ingredients

1 medium flatbread dough
(can be replaced with standard
pizza base)
½ cup tomato pizza sauce, sugar-free
½ cup spinach, chopped
1 cup skim milk
½ small onion, sliced
¼ cup fresh goat's cheese
3 oz mozzarella, sliced
1 tbsp oregano, dried
1 tsp salt
1 tbsp olive oil
7 olives
¼ medium-sized eggplant, sliced
½ large tomato, sliced

Preparation

Preheat the oven to 350 degrees.
Combine spinach and milk in a blender and pulse until smooth. Set aside.
Lay the flatbread on a baking sheet. Spread the sauce over the dough and sprinkle with oregano.
Now add the creamy spinach mixture, goat's cheese, and mozzarella.
Make a final layer with sliced onions, tomato, and eggplant.
Bake for 12-15 minutes. Remove from the oven and top with olives.

Serve immediately.

Total Daily Nutritional Facts

Calories: 287	Protein: 15.3g	Total Fat: 17.5g	Trans Fat: 0g
Dietary Fiber: 2.4g 9%	Sugars: 5.4g	Cholesterol: 27mg 10%	Sodium: 1144mg 50%
Saturated Fat: 6.8g 34%	Total Carbs: 18.2g 6%		

Wild Berries Pancakes

Preparation Time
5 min

Cooking Time
4-5 min

Ingredients

1 cup buckwheat flour
2 tsp baking powder
1¼ cup skim milk
1 egg
½ tsp salt
1 tsp vanilla sugar
1 tsp strawberry extract
1 cup Greek yogurt
1 cup fresh wild berries

Preparation

In a medium-sized mixing bowl, combine the milk and egg. Beat well with a whisking attachment on high - until foamy. Gradually add flour and continue to beat until combined.

Now add baking powder, salt, and vanilla sugar. Continue to beat on high for 3 more minutes.

Heat a large non-stick skillet and carefully brush with some oil. Spoon 2-3 tablespoons of batter onto the skillet and cook until the surface of the batter has some bubbles, for approximately 1-2 minutes. Gently flip with a spatula and continue to cook for 2 more minutes.

Top each pancake with one tablespoon of Greek yogurt and wild berries. Sprinkle with strawberry extract and serve immediately.

Total Daily Nutritional Facts

Calories: 135	Protein: 8.6g	Total Fat: 2.1g 3%	Trans Fat: 0g
Dietary Fiber: 2.6g 9%,	Sugars: 6.4g	Cholesterol: 30mg 11%	Sodium: 246mg 11%
Saturated Fat: 0.9g 4%	Total Carbs: 21.5g 7%		

Boiled Eggs with Steamed Vegetables

Serves
2 Persons

Preparation Time
5 min

Cooking Time
20 min

Ingredients

1 hard-boiled egg
1 carrot, finely chopped
½ cup green peas, pre-cooked
½ red bell pepper, sliced
½ cup green beans
1 tbsp olive oil
¼ cup fresh parsley leaves, finely chopped
½ tsp sea salt
1 tsp Italian Seasoning mix

Preparation

Gently place the egg in a pot of boiling water. Cook for 12 minutes. Drain and set aside to cool.
Grease a large, non-stick skillet with olive oil. Heat up over medium-high heat and add finely chopped carrot, green peas, sliced bell pepper, and green beans. Season with salt and Italian seasoning mix and give it a good stir. Stir-fry for 10 minutes.
Finally, add fresh parsley and toss well to combine. Remove from the heat and transfer to a serving plate. Now, peel the egg and slice in half. Serve with vegetables.
Optionally, sprinkle with some fresh lime juice and garnish with some olives.

Total Daily Nutritional Facts

Calories: 219	Protein: 6g	Total Fat: 9.5g 12%	Trans Fat: 0g
Dietary Fiber: 4.2g 15%	Sugars: 6.2g	Cholesterol: 82mg 30%	Sodium: 337mg 15%
Saturated Fat: 1.7g 9%	Total Carbs: 13.6g 5%		

Homemade Salmon Spread

Serves

4 Persons

Preparation Time

10 min

Ingredients

4 oz smoked salmon, minced
¼ cup cream cheese
1 tbsp sour cream
1 tbsp freshly squeezed lemon juice
2 garlic cloves, crushed
¼ cup fresh parsley leaves, finely chopped
½ tsp salt

Preparation

Combine cream cheese with sour cream in a large mixing bowl fitted with a whisking attachment. Beat well for one minute and then add smoked salmon, lemon juice, crushed garlic, parsley, and salt.
Continue to beat for 2 more minutes with a paddle attachment.
Transfer to clean glass jars with tight lids and keep in the refrigerator for up to 10 days.

Total Daily Nutritional Facts

Calories: 95	Protein: 6.6g	Total Fat: 7g 9%	Trans Fat: 0g
Dietary Fiber: 0.2g 1%	Sugars: 0.2g	Cholesterol: 24mg 9%	Sodium: 905mg 39%
Saturated Fat: 3.9g 19%	Total Carbs: 1.3g 0%		

Oven-Baked Chicken Risotto

Serves
5 Persons

Preparation Time
1 hr 30 min

Cooking Time
50 min

Ingredients

5 small chicken drumsticks (about 12oz)
1 cup brown rice
1 cup Greek yogurt
1 medium-sized onion, finely chopped
¼ cup fresh parsley leaves, finely chopped
1 tbsp cumin seeds
1 tbsp fresh mint
leaves, finely chopped
2 tbsp freshly squeezed lemon juice
1 lemon, sliced
½ cup olive oil plus two tablespoons for frying

Preparation

Rinse the meat under cold running water and pat dry with a kitchen towel. Place in a medium-sized bowl. Add olive oil, Greek yogurt, parsley, cumin seeds, mint leaves, and lemon juice.

Toss well to combine and wrap tightly in plastic foil. Refrigerate for one hour.

Meanwhile, place rice in a deep, heavy-bottomed pot. Add three cups of water and bring it to a boil. Reduce the heat to medium-low and cook until all the liquid evaporates. Stir occasionally.

Grease a large non-stick pan with two tablespoons of olive oil and add onions. Stir-fry until translucent. Remove from the heat and set aside.

Remove the chicken from the refrigerator and drain from the marinade, but make sure to reserve it. Pat dry with some kitchen paper and place in the frying pan with onions. Add three cups of water and cover with the lid. Cook for 20 minutes, over medium-high heat.

Preheat the oven to 400 degrees. Spread three tablespoons of the marinade over a round baking pan and add rice. Cover cooked chicken drumsticks and top with sliced lemon.

Bake for 15 minutes, or until nice and crispy. Remove from the heat and serve immediately.

Total Daily Nutritional Facts

Calories: 398	Protein: 26.3g	Sugars: 3g	Trans Fat: 0g
Dietary Fiber: 2.4g 9%	Total Carbs: 34.6g 12%	Sodium: 75mg 3%	Cholesterol: 62mg 23%
Saturated Fat: 3.5g 18%	Total Fat: 17.3g 22%		

Grilled Garlic Leeks

Serves
4 Persons

Preparation Time
15 min

Cooking Time
7 min

Ingredients

5 leeks, cut into 2-inch long pieces
4 garlic cloves, crushed
½ tsp sea salt
¼ cup extra virgin olive oil
3 tbsp freshly squeezed lemon juice

Preparation

Rinse the leeks under cold running water and drain in a large colander. Place on a clean work surface and cut into 2-inch long pieces. Set aside.
Preheat a large, non-stick grill pan over medium-high heat.
In a small bowl, combine olive oil with sea salt and garlic.
 Brush the mixture over chopped leeks and grill for 5 minutes. Stir well and cook for 2 more minutes.
Sprinkle with fresh lemon juice before serving.

Total Daily Nutritional Facts

Calories: 183	Protein: 2g	Total Fat: 13g 17%	Trans Fat: 0g
Dietary Fiber: 2.1g 8%	Sugars: 4.6g	Cholesterol: 0mg 0%	Sodium: 259mg 11%
Saturated Fat: 1.9g 10%	Total Carbs: 17g 6%		

Adana Kebab

Serves	Preparation Time	Cooking Time
4 Persons	**15** min	**14** min

Ingredients

7 oz ground lamb
7 oz ground veal
2 small onions, finely chopped
1 red bell pepper, finely chopped
2 garlic cloves, crushed
1 tbsp extra virgin olive oil
1 tsp sumac
2 tsp coriander, ground
2 tsp cayenne pepper
2 tbsp all-purpose flour
½ tsp salt
¼ tsp black pepper

Preparation

Preheat a large grill pan over medium-high heat.
In a large bowl, combine ground lamb and ground veal. Add finely chopped onions, bell pepper, crushed garlic, olive oil, sumac, coriander, flour, cayenne pepper, salt, and black pepper.
Mix with your hands until well combined and shape about half-inch thick kebabs. Place on a grill and cook for 7 minutes on one side. Gently flip and continue to cook for 7 more minutes.

Total Daily Nutritional Facts

Calories: 251	Protein: 27.3g	Total Fat: 11.2g 14%	Trans Fat: 0g
Dietary Fiber: 1.6g 6%	Sugars: 3.1g	Cholesterol: 96mg 35%	Sodium: 373mg 16%
Saturated Fat: 3.4g 17%	Total Carbs: 9.6g 3%		

Fruit Salad

Serves
3 Persons

Preparation Time
10 min

Cooking Time
2 min

Ingredients

1 cup blueberries
½ cup cranberries
½ cup blackberries
1 cup strawberries
1 kiwi, sliced
½ cup freshly squeezed   orange juice
2 tbsp freshly squeezed lemon juice
1 tsp powdered stevia
1 tsp vanilla extract

Preparation

In a small saucepan, combine orange juice, lemon juice, stevia, and vanilla extract. Bring it to a boil and briefly cook – for one minute. Remove from the heat and cool completely.
Meanwhile, rinse the fruit under cold running water and drain in a large colander. Transfer to a serving bowl and drizzle with chilled orange juice.

Refrigerate for at least an hour before serving.

Total Daily Nutritional Facts

Calories: 104	Protein: 1.7g	Total Fat: 0.7g 1%	Trans Fat: 0g
Dietary Fiber: 5g 18%	Sugars: 15.1g	Cholesterol: 0g 0%	Sodium: 4mg 0%
Saturated Fat: 0.1g 1%	Total Carbs: 23.1g 8%		

Orange Marinated Grilled Catfish

Serves	Preparation Time	Cooking Time
6 Persons	**45** min	**25** min

Ingredients

1 lb young flathead catfish
1 cup freshly squeezed orange juice
¼ cup freshly squeezed lemon juice
½ cup extra virgin olive oil
1 tbsp dried thyme
1 tbsp dried rosemary
1 tsp chili flakes
1 tsp peppercorn
1 tsp sea salt
3 oranges, sliced
1 tsp salt

Preparation

Preheat the oven to 350 degrees. Line some parchment paper over a baking sheet and set aside.
Rinse the oranges well and place on a clean work surface. Using a sharp paring knife, slice oranges into ¼ - inch thick slices. Place onto a baking sheet.
Now combine the orange juice with lemon juice, olive oil, thyme, rosemary, chili flakes, peppercorn, and salt. Generously brush the fish with this mixture and refrigerate for 30 minutes.
Remove from the refrigerator and drain but reserve the marinade. Place the fish onto a baking sheet and drizzle with some of the marinade – about three tablespoons.
Bake for 25 minutes, turning once. If necessary, brush with some more marinade.

Serve warm.

Total Daily Nutritional Facts

Calories: 306	Protein: 12.7g	Total Fat: 22.5g 29%	Trans Fat: 0g
Dietary Fiber: 2.8g 10%	Sugars: 12.3g	Cholesterol: 43g 16%	Sodium: 422mg 18%
Saturated Fat: 3.9g 20%	Total Carbs: 16.2g 5%		

Beef Patties with Garlic Dip

Serves
4 Persons

Preparation Time
45 min

Cooking Time
6-8 min

Ingredients

1lb lean ground beef
1 large egg
½ cup onions, finely chopped
2 garlic cloves, crushed
¼ cup oil
1 tsp salt
¼ tsp black pepper
¼ cup parsley leaves, finely chopped
¼ cup skim milk

Preparation

In a medium-sized bowl, combine ground beef with finely chopped onions, garlic, oil, salt, pepper, parsley, and milk.

Whisk in one egg and mix well to combine. Tightly wrap the bowl with aluminum foil and refrigerate for 30-40 minutes.

 Remove the meat from the refrigerator and gently shape into one-inch-thick patties, about 4-inches in diameter.

Grease a large, non-stick skillet with some olive oil. Heat up to medium-high heat and cook patties for 3-4 minutes on each side.

Total Daily Nutritional Facts

Calories: 364	Protein: 36.9g	Total Fat: 22g 28%	Trans Fat: 0g
Dietary Fiber: 0.5g 2%	Sugars: 1.5g	Cholesterol: 148g 54%	Sodium: 658mg 30%
Saturated Fat: 4.8g 24%	Total Carbs: 3g 1%		

Poached Eggs with Leeks

Serves
3 Persons

Preparation Time
10 min

Cooking Time
18-20 min

Ingredients

5 leeks, chopped into one-inch long pieces
1 cup spinach, finely chopped
3 eggs
2 tbsp extra virgin olive oil
1 tsp mustard seeds
1 tbsp Italian seasoning mix

Preparation

Rinse the spinach under cold water and place in a deep pot. Pour enough water to cover and bring it to a boil. Cook for 2 minutes and remove from the heat. Drain again and set aside.

Grease a large skillet with olive oil. Heat up over medium-high heat and add mustard seeds and leeks. Stir-fry for 5 minutes and then add spinach. Reduce the heat to medium-low and cook for 10 minutes. Gently crack three eggs and cook for 3 more minutes. Season with Italian seasoning mix and remove from the heat.

Serve warm.

Total Daily Nutritional Facts

Calories: 284	Protein: 8.3g	Total Fat: 14.5g 19%	Trans Fat: 0g
Dietary Fiber: 3.1g 11%	Sugars: 6.6g	Cholesterol: 164g 60%	Sodium: 206mg 9%
Saturated Fat: 2.8g 14%	Total Carbs: 14.5g 19%		

Baked Trout Fillet

Serves
6 Persons

Preparation Time
1 hr 10 min

Cooking Time
20 min

Ingredients

2 lbs trout fillets, skin on
½ cup olive oil
¼ cup apple cider vinegar
1 red onion, sliced
1 lemon, sliced
3 garlic cloves, crushed
1 tbsp fresh rosemary, chopped
1 tbsp dill sprigs, chopped
½ sea salt
¼ tsp freshly ground black pepper

Preparation

In a medium-sized bowl, combine olive oil with apple cider, sliced onions, crushed garlic, rosemary, dill, sea salt, and pepper. Submerge the fillets in this mixture and refrigerate for 1 hour.
Preheat the oven to 350 degrees. Remove the fish from the refrigerator and place into the baking dish along with the marinade and lemon slices.
Bake for 15 minutes, turn over and cook for another 5 minutes.

Total Daily Nutritional Facts

Calories: 373	Protein: 32.6g	Total Fat: 25g 32%	Trans Fat: 0g
Dietary Fiber: 1g 4%	Sugars: 1.1g	Cholesterol: 0g 0%	Sodium: 42mg 2%
Saturated Fat: 2.4g 12%	Total Carbs: 3.9g 1%		

Chicken Fillets

Serves
4 Persons

Preparation Time
15 min

Cooking Time
14 min

Ingredients

1 lb chicken breast, boneless and skinless
¼ cup olive oil
¼ cup apple cider vinegar
1 tbsp fresh rosemary, finely chopped
1 tsp dried oregano
1 tsp cayenne pepper
½ tsp sea salt

Preparation

Preheat a large grill pan or an electric grill to medium-high heat.

Rinse the meat and pat dry with some kitchen paper. Using a sharp cutting knife, slice into half-inch thick slices. Set aside.

Combine the olive oil, apple cider, rosemary, oregano, cayenne, and salt. Generously brush each fillet with this mixture and grill for 7 minutes on each side. If necessary, brush with some more oil while cooking. This will prevent sticking.

Total Daily Nutritional Facts

Calories: 246	Protein: 24.2g	Total Fat: 15.7g 20%	Trans Fat: 0g
Dietary Fiber: 0.6g 2%	Sugars: 0.1g	Cholesterol: 73g 26%	Sodium: 293mg 13%
Saturated Fat: 1.9g 9%	Total Carbs: 1.2g 0%		

Acai Bowl

Serves
2 Persons

Preparation Time
5 min

Ingredients

1 cup frozen strawberries
2 tbsp acai powder
1 cup milk
1 tsp honey
2 tbsp cranberry oats
2 tbsp cranberries
2 tbsp blueberries
2 almonds
2-3 walnuts
1 tsp chia seeds

Preparation

Combine milk, acai powder, frozen strawberries, and honey in a blender or a food processor. Pulse well, until completely smooth.
Transfer to a serving bowl and top with cranberry oats, cranberries, blueberries, almonds, walnuts, and chia seeds.

Total Daily Nutritional Facts

Calories: 195	Protein: 6.2g	Total Fat: 8.2g 11%	Trans Fat: 0g
Dietary Fiber: 3.6g 13%	Sugars: 16.2g	Cholesterol: 10g 4%	Sodium: 94mg 4%
Saturated Fat: 2.8g 14%	Total Carbs: 25.6g 9%		

Raspberry Smoothie

Serves	Preparation Time
2 Persons	**5** min

Ingredients

1 cup raspberries
¼ cup blueberries
5 almonds
1 tsp honey
1 cup skim milk
½ cup water

Preparation

Combine the ingredients in a blender and pulse until completely smooth.

Serve cold.

Total Daily Nutritional Facts

Calories: 115	Protein: 5.5g	Total Carbs: 19.5g 6%	Sugars: 13.5g
Saturated Fat: 0.1g 1%	Total Fat: 2g 3%	Trans Fat: 0g	Sodium: 66mg 3%
Dietary Fiber: 4.8g 17%	Cholesterol: 2g 1%		

Fish Stew with Homemade Polenta

Serves
8 Persons

Preparation Time
20 min

Cooking Time
55 min

Ingredients

1 cup fire roasted tomatoes, diced
2 lbs mixed fish (mackerel, Whiting fish, salmon)
1 tbsp dried basil
6 cups fish stock
6 tbsp tomato paste
6 celery stalks, chopped
3 carrots, sliced
3 tbsp olive oil
1 onion, finely chopped
6 garlic cloves, crushed

Preparation

In a large skillet, heat up the olive oil over medium-high heat.
Add onions and stir-fry until translucent. Now add garlic, carrots, celery stalks, tomato paste, and basil. Give it a good stir and continue to cook for two more minutes.
Finally, add fire-roasted tomatoes and 1 cup of fish stock. Bring it to a boil and remove from the heat. Transfer to a deep, heavy-bottomed pot. Add fish and the remaining fish stock. Cover and cook over medium heat for 45 minutes.

Total Daily Nutritional Facts

Calories: 324	Protein: 35.4g	Total Fat: 16.4g 21%	Trans Fat: 0g
Dietary Fiber: 1.9g 7	Sugars: 3.7g	Cholesterol: 86g 31%	Sodium: 419mg 18%
Saturated Fat: 2.8g 14%	Total Carbs: 7.6g 3%		

Homemade polenta (optional)

Serves   Preparation Time
2 Persons   **5** min

Ingredients

17oz corn flour
5 cups of water
5 tbsp of olive oil
½ tsp salt

Preparation

Bring five cups of water to the boiling point.
Add salt, olive oil, and reduce the heat to medium. Slowly whisk in the corn flour.
Cook until the mixture thickens, stirring often. Remove from the heat and serve.

Total Daily Nutritional Facts

Calories: 234	Protein: 3.3g	Total Carbs: 37g 12%	Sugars: 0.3g
Saturated Fat: 1.3g 6%	Total Fat: 8.9g 11%	Trans Fat: 0g	Sodium: 122mg 5%
Dietary Fiber: 3.5g 13%	Cholesterol: 0g %0		

Cold Cauliflower Salad

Serves
4 Persons

Preparation Time
15 min

Cooking Time
35 min

Ingredients

1 lb cauliflower florets
1 lb broccoli
4 garlic cloves, crushed
3 tbsp of extra virgin olive oil
1 tbsp freshly squeezed lemon juice
1 tbsp dried rosemary, crushed
¼ tsp salt

Preparation

Rinse the vegetables under cold running water and drain in a large colander. Using a sharp knife, cut into bite-sized pieces.

Place in a deep pot and pour in enough water to cover. Bring it to a boil and cook until fork-tender, for 15-20 minutes. Remove from the heat and drain.

In a large skillet, heat up the olive oil over medium-high heat. Add garlic and stir-fry for two minutes. Now add chopped cauliflower and broccoli and give it a good stir. Season with salt and rosemary. Cook for 7-10 minutes.

Remove from the heat and transfer to a serving plate. Cool to a room temperature and then refrigerate for one hour.

Drizzle with lemon juice before serving.

Total Daily Nutritional Facts

Calories: 165	Protein: 5.7g	Total Fat: 11.2g 14%	Trans Fat: 0g
Dietary Fiber: 6.2g 22%	Sugars: 4.8g	Cholesterol: 0g %0	Sodium: 220mg 10%
Saturated Fat: 1.6g 8%,	Total Carbs: 15.1g 5%		

Poached Eggs with Tomato

Serves
2 Persons

Preparation Time
10 min

Cooking Time
20 min

Ingredients

1 lb tomatoes, peeled and roughly chopped
1 cup fire-roasted tomatoes, diced
1 onion, finely chopped
2 eggs
2 tbsp olive oil
½ tsp sea salt
1 tsp dried oregano
1 tsp brown sugar
¼ cup fresh parsley

Preparation

In a large skillet, heat up the olive oil over medium-high heat.
Add onions and stir-fry until translucent. Now add fresh tomatoes, fire-roasted tomatoes, salt, oregano, and sugar.Stir well and reduce the heat to medium-low. Cook for 15 minutes, stirring constantly.
Finally, crack two eggs and continue to cook until set. Sprinkle with some fresh parsley and serve.

Total Daily Nutritional Facts

Calories: 269	Protein: 9g	Total Fat: 19g 24%	Trans Fat: 0g
Dietary Fiber: 5.5g 20%	Sugars: 11.7g	Cholesterol: 164g 60%	Sodium: 673mg 29%
Saturated Fat: 3.5g 17%	Total Carbs: 19.2g 6%		

Spanish Cold Gazpacho Polenta

Serves	Preparation Time	Cooking Time
4 Persons	**5** min	**20-25** min

Ingredients

1 pound of fresh tomatoes, peeled and finely chopped
3 large cucumbers, finely chopped
3 spring onions, finely chopped
1 medium-sized red onion, finely chopped
2 tbsp olive oil
1 tbsp of tomato paste
½ tsp of salt
1 tbsp of ground cumin
¼ tsp of pepper
Fresh parsley, for serving

Preparation

Heat up the oil over medium-high heat. Add onions and stir-fry for 3-4 minutes.
Now add the tomatoes, tomato paste, cucumber, cumin, salt, and pepper. Cook for another five minutes, or until caramelized.
Add three cups of lukewarm water, reduce the heat to minimum and cook for about 15 minutes. Now add about 1 cup of water and bring it to a boil. Remove from the heat and garnish with fresh parsley. *Serve cold.*

Total Daily Nutritional Facts

Calories: 138	Protein: 3.4g	Total Fat: 7.9g 10%	Trans Fat: 0g
Dietary Fiber: 3.7g 13%	Sugars: 8.7g	Cholesterol: 0g 0%	Sodium: 310mg 13%
Saturated Fat: 1.1g 6%	Total Carbs: 17.5g 6%		

Chicken Pudding with Artichoke

Serves
4 Persons

Cooking Time
20-30 min

Preparation Time
15-20 min

Ingredients

1 lb dark and white chicken meat, cooked
2 artichokes
2 tbsp of butter, unsalted
2 tbsp of extra virgin olive oil
1 lemon, juiced
1 handful of fresh parsley leaves
1 tsp of pink Himalayan salt
¼ tsp of freshly ground black pepper
½ tsp of ground chili pepper, for topping

Total Daily Nutritional Facts

Calories: 369	Protein: 35.7g	Total Carbs: 10g 3%	Dietary Fiber: 4.8g 17%
Sugars: 1.2g	Total Fat: 21.3g 27%	Trans Fat: 0g	Cholesterol: 116g 42%
Saturated Fat: 7g 35%	Sodium: 360mg 16%		

Preparation

If possible, use organic chicken meat (breast and thighs). Thoroughly rinse the meat and pat dry with a kitchen paper. Using a sharp paring knife, cut the meat into smaller pieces and remove the bones. Rub with olive oil and set aside.

Heat the saute pan over medium-high heat. Turn the heat down slightly to medium and add the meat. Cook for about one minute to get it a little golden on one side. Then flip each piece, cover the pan with a thigh fitting lid and turn the heat to low. Cook for ten minutes without removing the lid. This will poach your meat from the inside out in its own juices. This is why it's important that the lid stays on all the time.

Now turn off the heat and let it sit for another ten minutes. It has to stay covered the whole time. Take the lid off the pan and set aside allowing the meat to cool for a while.

Meanwhile, prepare the artichoke. Cut the lemon into halves and squeeze the juice in a small bowl. Divide the juice in half and set aside.

Using a sharp paring knife, trim off the outer leaves until you reach the yellow and soft ones. Trim off the green outer skin around the artichoke base and stem. Make sure to remove the 'hairs' around the artichoke heart. They are inedible so simply throw them away. Cut artichoke into half-inch pieces. Rub with half of the lemon juice and place in a heavy-bottomed pot. Add enough water to cover and cook until completely fork-tender. Remove from the heat and drain. Chill for a while (to a room temperature). I like to cut each piece into thin strips, but this is optional.

Now combine artichoke with chicken meat in a large bowl. Stir in salt, pepper, and the remaining lemon juice. Melt the butter over medium heat and drizzle over pudding. Sprinkle with some chili pepper and parsley. Serve.

Marinated Sea Bream

Serves
4 Persons

Preparation Time
40 min

Cooking Time
14-16 min

Ingredients

2 lbs sea bream, cleaned
¼ cup olive oil
¼ cup freshly squeezed lemon juice
1 tbsp fresh rosemary sprigs
1 tbsp Italian seasoning mix
½ tsp sea salt
1 tsp garlic powder
2 tsp coriander, ground
2 tsp cayenne pepper
2 tbsp all-purpose flour
½ tsp salt
¼ tsp black pepper

Preparation

Remove the fish from the refrigerator and let it sit at the room temperature for at least 30 minutes before using. In a small bowl, combine olive oil with lemon juice, rosemary sprigs, Italian seasoning, sea salt, and garlic powder. Brush each fish generously with this mixture and wrap tightly with plastic foil. Refrigerate for 30 minutes before grilling.

Preheat a large, non-stick grill pan to a medium-high heat. Remove the fish from the refrigerator and pat-dry with a kitchen towel.

Grill for 7-8 minutes on each side.

Total Daily Nutritional Facts

Calories: 430

Protein: 54.3g

Total Fat: 20.5g 26%

Trans Fat: 0g

Dietary Fiber: 0.5g 2%

Sugars: 0.5g

Cholesterol: 60g 22%

Sodium: 413mg 18%

Saturated Fat: 2g 10%

Total Carbs: 3.1g 1%

Almond Balls

Serves
10 Persons

Preparation Time
5 min

Ingredients

1 cup rolled oats
½ cup toasted almonds, finely chopped
2 tbsp cocoa powder, sugar-free
1 cup skim milk
1 tbsp powdered stevia
1 cup dark chocolate, melted

Preparation

In a medium-sized bowl, combine rolled oats with toasted almonds, cocoa powder, and stevia. Mix well and gradually add milk until you get a slightly sticky mass.
Shape approximately 1-inch diameter balls and set aside.
Place the chocolate in a small, heatproof bowl. Sit over a pan of boiling water and allow it to melt naturally. Dip each ball in chocolate and refrigerate for 30 minutes.
Optionally, sprinkle with coconut flour or powdered sugar.

Total Daily Nutritional Facts

Calories: 160	Protein: 4.4g	Total Fat: 8g 10%	Trans Fat: 0g
Dietary Fiber: 2.3g 8%	Sugars: 10.2g	Cholesterol: 4g 2%	Sodium: 27mg 1%
Saturated Fat: 3.8g 19%	Total Carbs: 18.3g 6%		

Spring Salad with Cranberries

Serves
1 Persons

Preparation Time
10 min

Ingredients

2 oz fresh arugula
1 orange, peeled and sectioned
5-6 fresh strawberries
¼ cup of fresh cranberries
1 tbsp of honey
3 tbsp of fresh lime juice
5 tbsp of fresh orange juice
¼ tsp of ground cinnamon

Preparation

Whisk together 1 tablespoon of honey with fresh lime juice, fresh orange juice, and ground cinnamon. Soak each piece of fruit in this mixture and transfer to a serving platter. Add fresh arugula and mix well. Serve cold.

Total Daily Nutritional Facts

Calories: 239	Protein: 4.6g	Total Fat: 1g 1%	Trans Fat: 0g
Dietary Fiber: 0.1g 1%	Sugars: 46.4g	Cholesterol: 0g 0%	Sodium: 21mg 1%
Saturated Fat: 0.1g 1%	Total Carbs: 57.2g 19%		

Blueberry Yogurt with Hazelnuts

Serves
2 Persons

Preparation Time
5 min

Ingredients

1 cup Greek yogurt
¼ cup blueberries
1 tsp blueberry extract, sugar-free
1 tbsp honey
¼ tsp cinnamon, ground
¼ cup hazelnuts
3 figs

Preparation

Place Greek yogurt, blueberries, blueberry extract, honey, and cinnamon in a blender or a food processor. Blend until smooth, for 30 seconds. Transfer the mixture to a serving bowl and freeze for 30 minutes. Top with fresh figs and hazelnuts. Optionally, add one teaspoon of chia seeds.
Enjoy!

Total Daily Nutritional Facts

Calories: 248

Dietary Fiber: 4.3g 15%

Saturated Fat: 2g 10%

Protein: 12.5g

Sugars: 28.5g

Total Carbs: 35.3g 12%

Total Fat: 8g 10%

Cholesterol: 5g 2%

Trans Fat: 0g

Sodium: 36mg 2%

Pepper Meat

Serves
6 Persons

Preparation Time
35 min

Cooking Time
1hr 30 min

Ingredients

2 lbs beef fillet or another tender cut, cut into bite-sized pieces
5 medium-sized onions, peeled and finely chopped
3 tbsp tomato paste
2 tbsp olive oil
1 tbsp butter, softened
2 tbsp fresh parsley, finely chopped
½ tsp freshly ground black pepper
1 tsp salt

Preparation

Rinse the meat thoroughly under cold running water. Dry with a kitchen towel and place on a clean working surface.
Using a sharp knife cut the meat into bite-sized pieces.
Set aside.
Grease the bottom of a deep, heavy-bottomed pot with two tablespoons of olive oil.
Heat up over medium-high heat and add onions. Stir-fry for 2-3 minutes, until translucent.
Now add the meat and briefly brown, for 5 minutes. Stir well and add tomato paste, butter, salt, pepper, and parsley.
Pour in enough water to cover and reduce the heat to minimum.
Simmer for 1 hour 30 minutes, stirring occasionally.

Total Daily Nutritional Facts

Calories: 382	Protein: 47.3g	Total Fat: 16.2g 21%	Trans Fat: 0g
Dietary Fiber: 2.4g 9%	Sugars: 4.9g	Cholesterol: 140g 51%	Sodium: 513mg 22%
Saturated Fat: 5.5g 27%	Total Carbs: 10.3g 3%		

Greek Salad with Fresh Goat's Cheese

Serves	Preparation Time	Cooking Time
5 Persons	**35** min	**12** min

Ingredients

1 cup of fresh goat's cheese
1 egg, hard-boiled
½ cup of red cabbage, shredded
1 oz fresh lettuce, torn
1 tomato, roughly chopped
1 small onion, sliced
½ cucumber, peeled and sliced
½ red bell pepper, sliced
5 green olives
¼ cup olive oil
1 tsp mustard
1 tbsp finely chopped parsley
1 garlic clove, crushed
½ tsp salt
¼ tsp freshly ground black pepper

Preparation

In a small bowl, combine the olive oil with mustard, parsley, and garlic. Whisk together and refrigerate for 30 minutes.
Meanwhile, gently place the egg in a pot of boiling water.
Cook for 12 minutes. Remove from the heat and drain. Chill to a room temperature and then peel. Slice the egg and place in a large bowl.
Prepare the vegetables and add to a bowl. Drizzle with the olive oil mixture and serve.

Total Daily Nutritional Facts

Calories: 273	Protein: 10.7g	Total Fat: 23.7g 30%	Trans Fat: 0g
Dietary Fiber: 1.4g 5%	Sugars: 3.4g	Cholesterol: 64g 23%	Sodium: 528mg 23%
Saturated Fat: 10g 50%	Total Carbs: 6.5g 2%		

Panzanella to go

Serves
1 Persons

Preparation Time
15 min

Ingredients

2 slices bread (choose whole grain bread)
1 cup lettuce, torn
1 tomato, roughly chopped
1 onion, sliced
1 cucumber, sliced
1 tbsp extra virgin olive oil
1 tsp apple cider vinegar
1 tbsp Italian seasoning mix

Preparation

Wash and prepare the vegetables. Combine in a large bowl and season with olive oil, apple cider, and Italian seasoning.
Toss to combine and serve.

Total Daily Nutritional Facts

Calories: 277	Protein: 5.4g	Total Fat: 15.3g 20%	Trans Fat: 0g
Dietary Fiber: 2.4g 9%	Sugars: 12.7g	Cholesterol: 0g 0%	Sodium: 139mg 6%
Saturated Fat: 2.3g 11%	Total Carbs: 34.4g 11%		

Cold Okra Salad

Serves	Preparation Time	Cooking Time
6 Persons	**35** min	**1hr 30 min**

Ingredients

7 oz fresh okra, whole

7 oz bean sprouts, trimmed

½ cup green peas, pre-cooked

2 medium-sized carrots, sliced into strips

7 oz cherry tomatoes, whole

3.5 oz baby corn, whole

3 garlic cloves, crushed

3 tbsp extra virgin olive oil

¼ cup white wine

½ tsp sea salt

1 tbsp fresh rosemary, finely chopped

Preparation

Rinse the vegetables under cold running water and drain in a large colander.

Place carrots, peas, and okra in a pressure cooker. Pour in enough water to cover and seal the lid. Set the steam release handle and cook for 10-15 minutes, depending on the type of your cooker. You want the carrots and beans to be fork tender, but not overcooked.

Remove from the pressure cooker and set aside.

Heat up the oil in a large skillet, over medium-high heat. Add garlic and stir-fry for 2 minutes. Now add bean sprouts, carrots, beans, okra, cherry tomatoes, and baby corn. Stir-fry for 4-5 minutes and pour in white wine. Season with salt and rosemary, give it a good stir and continue to cook for 10 more minutes. Remove from the heat and chill completely before serving.

Total Daily Nutritional Facts

Calories: 294	Protein: 9.3g	Total Fat: 12.7g 16%	Trans Fat: 0g
Dietary Fiber: 7.9g 28%	Sugars: 9.1g	Cholesterol: 0g %0	Sodium: 286mg 12%
Saturated Fat: 1.9g 9%	Total Carbs: 40.3g 13%		

Marble Bread

Serves
6 Persons

Preparation Time
15 min

Cooking Time
20 min

Ingredients

1 cup all-purpose flour
1 ½ tsp baking powder
1 tbsp powdered stevia
½ tsp salt
1 tsp cherry extract, sugar-free
3 tbsp butter, softened
3 eggs
¼ cup cocoa powder, sugar-free
¼ cup heavy cream

Preparation

Preheat the oven to 400 degrees. Line an 8x8 inches square baking pan with some parchment paper and set aside. Combine all dry ingredients, except cocoa in a large mixing bowl.
Mix well to combine and add eggs, one at the time. Beat well with a dough hook attachment for one minute. Now add sour cream, butter, and cherry extract. Continue to beat for 3 more minutes.
Divide the mixture in half and add cocoa powder in one-half of the mixture. Pour the light batter into the baking pan and drizzle with cocoa dough to create a nice marble pattern.
Cook for 20 minutes, or until a toothpick inserted in the middle comes out clean.
Remove from the oven and cool to a room temperature.
Transfer to the refrigerator and chill completely before serving.

Total Daily Nutritional Facts

Calories: 151	Protein: 5.7g	Total Fat: 6.6g 9%	Trans Fat: 0g
Dietary Fiber: 1.7g 6%	Sugars: 0.3g	Cholesterol: 94g 34%	Sodium: 229mg 10%
Saturated Fat: 3.4g 17%	Total Carbs: 18.8g 6%		

Red Pollock Stew

5 Persons

20 min   35 min

Ingredients

1 lb pollock fillet
4 garlic cloves, crushed
4 large tomatoes, peeled
2 bay leaves, whole
2 cups fish stock
1 teaspoon freshly ground black pepper
1 large onion, peeled and finely chopped
½ cup extra virgin olive oil
1 teaspoon sea salt

Preparation

Heat up the oil over medium-high heat. Add onions and garlic.
Stir-fry until translucent. Now add tomatoes and continue to cook stirring constantly until completely soft. Transfer the tomato mixture into a deep, heavy-bottomed pot. Add fish fillets, bay leaves, salt, and pepper.
Pour in fish stock and simmer for 35 minutes over medium heat.

Total Daily Nutritional Facts

Calories: 313	Protein: 21.8g	Total Fat: 22.1g 28%	Trans Fat: 0g
Dietary Fiber: 2.6g 9%	Sugars: 5.1g	Cholesterol: 45g 17%,	Sodium: 581mg 25%
Saturated Fat: 3.1g 16%	Total Carbs: 9.7g 3%		

Homemade Fig Jam

Serves
10 Persons

Preparation Time
30 min

Cooking Time
1 hr 10 min

Ingredients

2 lbs fresh figs, peeled and sliced in half
½ cup brown sugar
2 tbsp powdered stevia
½ cup freshly squeezed lemon juice
1 tsp ground cinnamon

Preparation

Place sugar and stevia in a deep pot and add enough water to cover. Bring it to a boil and cook until the sugar dissolves, stirring constantly.

Now add figs, lemon juice, and cinnamon. Pour in enough water to cover the figs. Reduce the heat to minimum and cover with the lid. Simmer for about an hour, stirring occasionally.

After about an hour, remove the pot from the heat and cool to a room temperature. Transfer to a food processor and blend until smooth.

Total Daily Nutritional Facts

Calories: 257	Protein: 3.1g	Total Fat: 0.9g 1%	Trans Fat: 0g
Dietary Fiber: 9.1g 32%	Sugars: 50.8g	Cholesterol: 0g 0%	Sodium: 14mg 1%
Saturated Fat: 0.2g 1%	Total Carbs: 65.5g 22%		

Classic Ragout Soup

Serves	Preparation Time	Cooking Time
6 Persons	**20** min	**60** min

Ingredients

1 lb lamb chops (1 inch thick)
1 cup of peas, rinsed
4 medium-sized carrots, peeled and finely chopped
3 small onions, peeled and finely chopped
1 large potato, peeled and finely chopped
1 large tomato, peeled and roughly chopped
3 tbsp of extra virgin olive oil
1 tbsp of cayenne pepper
1 tsp of salt
½ tsp of freshly ground black pepper

Preparation

Grease a deep, heavy-bottomed pot with three tablespoons of olive oil. Heat up over medium-high heat and add onions. Stir-fry until translucent. Now add carrots and continue to cook for five minutes, stirring constantly. Remove from the heat.

Rinse the meat and cut into bite-sized pieces. Place in the pot along with the remaining ingredients. Give it a good stir and pour in 3 cups of water (or beef broth).

Bring it to a boil and reduce the heat to minimum. Simmer for one hour, stirring occasionally. You want the meat and vegetables to be fork-tender but not overcooked.

Optionally, stir in one tablespoon of Greek yogurt before serving.
Enjoy!

Total Daily Nutritional Facts

Calories: 307	Protein: 24.9g	Total Fat: 13g 17%	Trans Fat: 0g
Dietary Fiber: 5g 18%	Sugars: 6.2g	Cholesterol: 68g 25%	Sodium: 481mg 21%
Saturated Fat: 3.1g 15%	Total Carbs: 23.3g 8%		

Chicken Drumstick Salad

Serves
4 Persons

Preparation Time
45 min

Cooking Time
35 min

Ingredients

4 small chicken drumsticks (about 1 pound)
7 oz button mushrooms, whole
1 medium-sized tomato, roughly chopped
2 oz lettuce
1 cup kalamata olives
1 cucumber, sliced
3 tbsp olive oil
1 tbsp Dijon mustard
¼ cup white wine
1 tsp freshly squeezed lemon juice
1 tbsp Italian seasoning mix
1 tsp salt

Preparation

In a small bowl, combine Dijon mustard with 2 tablespoons of olive oil, Italian seasoning mix, white wine, and salt. Stir well and brush the meat with this mixture. Wrap in aluminum foil and refrigerate for 30 minutes. Meanwhile, grease a large, non-stick skillet with the remaining oil. Add button mushrooms and cook for 10 minutes, stirring occasionally.
Remove from the heat and cool to a room temperature.
Wash and prepare the vegetables. Place in a serving bowl. Add mushrooms and stir well. Set aside.
Preheat the oven to 350 degrees. Line some parchment paper over a baking pan and set aside.
Remove the drumsticks from the refrigerator and transfer into a baking pan along with the marinade. Cook for 35 minutes, turning once. When done, remove the meat from the oven and chill to a room temperature.
Serve with vegetables.
Optionally, drizzle with some more olive oil before serving.

Total Daily Nutritional Facts

Protein: 15.5g	Total Carbs: 9g 3%	Saturated Fat: 2.7g 14%	Total Fat: 17.2g 22%
Calories: 283	Trans Fat: 0g	Cholesterol: 40g 15%	Sodium: 1043mg 45%
Dietary Fiber: 2.6g 9%	Sugars: 3.5g		

Grilled Eel with Garlic

Serves
2 Persons

Preparation Time
40 min

Cooking Time
11-12 min

Ingredients

1 lb eel, whole
1 tsp pink Himalayan salt
½ cup extra virgin olive oil
½ cup white wine
1 tbsp thyme, dried
1 tsp rosemary, dried
1 tbsp cilantro, finely chopped

Preparation

In a large bowl, combine olive oil with wine, salt, thyme, rosemary, and cilantro. Stir well. Generously brush the fish with this mixture and refrigerate for 30 minutes (up to 2 hours).
Remove the fish from the refrigerator and drain making sure to reserve the marinade.
Preheat a lightly oiled grill to high heat. Place eel on the grill and cook for 6-7 minutes. Gently flip and continue to grill for 5 more minutes. Optionally, brush the fish with some more marinade while cooking.

Total Daily Nutritional Facts

Calories: 394	Protein: 15.2g	Total Fat: 34.8g 45%	Trans Fat: 0g
Dietary Fiber: 0.4g 1%	Sugars: 0.2g	Cholesterol: 103g 37%	Sodium: 188mg 8%
Saturated Fat: 5.6g 28%	Total Carbs: 1.4g 0%		

Cherry Smoothie

Serves
2 Persons

Preparation Time
5 min

Ingredients

1 cup fresh cherries, pits removed
1 cup coconut water
¼ cup freshly squeezed beet juice
1 tbsp honey
¼ tsp cinnamon

Preparation

Combine the ingredients in a blender and pulse until completely smooth.
Serve Cold.

Total Daily Nutritional Facts

Calories: 154	Protein: 1.6g	Total Carbs: 37.1g 12%	Sugars: 14.5g
Saturated Fat: 0.2g 1%	Total Fat: 0.3g 0%	Trans Fat: 0g	Sodium: 152mg 7%
Dietary Fiber: 1.9g 7%	Cholesterol: 0g 0%		

Boiled Potatoes with Spring Onions and Olive Oil

Serves
2 Persons

Preparation Time
10 min

Cooking Time
20 min

Ingredients

2 medium-sized potatoes, boiled
5 spring onions, finely chopped
1 red onion, sliced
2 tbsp olive oil
¼ tsp sea salt
¼ tsp freshly ground black pepper

Preparation

Peel the potatoes and rinse under cold running water. Pat dry with a kitchen towel and slice into half-inch thick slices. Place in a deep, heavy-bottomed pot and pour in enough water to cover. Bring it to a boil and reduce the heat to medium. Cook until fork-tender, for 15 minutes.

Remove from the heat and chill to a room temperature. Transfer the potatoes to a serving bowl. Add sliced onions and spring onions. Toss well to combine and season with olive oil, salt, and pepper.

Refrigerate for 30 minutes before serving.

Total Daily Nutritional Facts

Calories: 302	Protein: 4.9g	Total Fat: 14.4g 18%	Trans Fat: 0g
Dietary Fiber: 7.3g 26%	Sugars: 5.7g	Cholesterol: 0g 0%	Sodium: 255mg 11%
Saturated Fat: 2.1g 10%	Total Carbs: 41.5g 14%		

Thick Lentil Soup

Serves
5 Persons

Preparation Time
10 min

Cooking Time
12 min

Ingredients

1 cup of brown lentils
1 large onion, peeled and finely chopped
2 large carrots, sliced
1 large potato, peeled and chopped
2 large celery stalks, sliced
7 oz bacon, sliced
3 tbsp extra virgin olive oil
3 large garlic cloves, minced
4 cups beef broth
1 tsp thyme, dried
1 tsp salt
¼ tsp freshly ground black pepper

Preparation

Heat up the oil in a deep pot over medium-high heat. Add onions, garlic, and celery. Stir-fry for five minutes.
Now add lentils, sliced carrot, chopped potato, and bacon. Season with salt, pepper, and thyme. Add broth and give it a good stir.
Bring it to a boil and then reduce the heat to medium-low.
Cook until lentils completely soften, for 45 minutes. Stir occasionally.
Remove from the heat and serve warm.

Total Daily Nutritional Facts

Calories: 452	Protein: 24.5g	Total Fat: 26.4g 34%	Trans Fat: 0g
Dietary Fiber: 6.7g 14%	Sugars: 4.9g	Cholesterol: 44g 16%	Sodium: 1807mg 79%
Saturated Fat: 7g 35%	Total Carbs: 29.4g 10%		

Mediterranean Grilled Shrimps

Serves
4 Persons

Preparation Time
10 min

Cooking Time
5 min

Ingredients

1 lb fresh large shrimps, whole
3 tbsp extra-virgin olive oil
3 garlic cloves, crushed
3 tbsp of fresh parsley, finely chopped
1 tsp sea salt

Preparation

Make sure you use the best, extra-virgin olive oil to get maximum flavor.
Rinse the shrimps and drain in a large colander. Pat dry with a kitchen towel and set aside.
Heat up the oil in a large grill pan over medium-high heat. Add shrimps and grill for 3 minutes on each side. Remove from the heat and transfer to a serving plate.
Top with some crushed garlic and fresh parsley before serving. Season with sea salt and enjoy!

Total Daily Nutritional Facts

Calories: 186	Protein: 21.5g	Total Fat: 10.5g 14%	Trans Fat: 0g
Dietary Fiber: 0.1g 1%	Sugars: 0g	Cholesterol: 162g 59%	Sodium: 202mg 9%
Saturated Fat: 1.5g 8%	Total Carbs: 3g 1%		

Tomato Omelet

Preparation Time
10 min

Cooking Time
20 min

Ingredients

1 lb tomatoes, peeled and roughly chopped
1 tbsp tomato paste
1 tsp brown sugar
1 cup fresh goat's cheese
3 eggs
3 tbsp olive oil
1 tbsp Italian seasoning mix
¼ cup fresh parsley, finely chopped
¼ tsp salt

Preparation

Heat up the oil in a large skillet. Add tomatoes, sugar, Italian seasoning, parsley, and salt.
Give it a good stir and simmer over medium heat until tomatoes soften, for 15 minutes. Stir occasionally.
Meanwhile whisk together eggs and goat's cheese. Optionally, add some more salt. Pour the mixture into the frying pan and give it a good stir. Cook for 3 more minutes.
Remove from the heat and serve warm.

Total Daily Nutritional Facts

Calories: 298	Protein: 3.1g	Total Fat: 24.7g 32%	Trans Fat: 0g
Dietary Fiber: 1.6g 6%	Sugars: 5.4g	Cholesterol: 151mg 55%	Sodium: 423mg 18%
Saturated Fat: 9.9g 49%	Total Carbs: 8.2g 3%		

Anchovy and Mussels Risotto

Serves
4 Persons

Preparation Time
15 min

Cooking Time
25 min

Ingredients

1 cup rice (choose brown rice)
7 oz mussels
1 onion, finely chopped
1 garlic clove, crushed
1 tbsp dried rosemary, finely chopped
¼ cup salted capers
1 tsp chili pepper, ground
½ tsp salt
3 tbsp olive oil
4 salted anchovies

Preparation

Place the rice in a deep pot. Add three cups of water and bring it to a boil. Reduce the heat to minimum and simmer until all the liquid evaporates, for 15 minutes. Stir occasionally. Remove from the heat and set aside.

Heat up the olive oil over medium heat. Add finely chopped onion and garlic. Stir-fry until translucent. Now add the mussels, rosemary, chili pepper, and salt. Continue to cook for 7-10 minutes. Remove from the heat and combine with rice.

Add capers, top with anchovies, and mix well.

Total Daily Nutritional Facts

Calories: 327	Protein: 11.4g	Total Fat: 12.3g 16%	Trans Fat: 0g
Dietary Fiber: 1.6g 6%	Sugars: 1.3g	Cholesterol: 14mg 5%	Sodium: 437mg 19%
Saturated Fat: 1.9g 9%	Total Carbs: 42.5g 14%		

Tuna Pizza

Serves
4 Persons

Preparation Time
10 min

Cooking Time
15 min

Ingredients

1 cup canned tuna, oil-free
½ cup mozzarella cheese, shredded
¼ cup goat's cheese
3 tbsp olive oil
1 tbsp tomato paste
1 tsp dried oregano
½ tsp dried rosemary
14 oz pizza crust
1 cup olives, optional

Preparation

Preheat the oven to 400 degrees. Line some parchment paper over a round baking pan and place the pizza crust in it.

In a small bowl, combine olive oil with tomato paste, oregano, and rosemary. Whisk together and spread the mixture over the crust.

Sprinkle with goat's cheese, mozzarella, and tuna. Optionally, top with some olives and bake for 15 minutes.

Total Daily Nutritional Facts

Calories: 495

Protein: 28.4g

Total Fat: 21.8g 28%

Trans Fat: 0g

Dietary Fiber: 1.9g 7%

Sugars: 6.8g

Cholesterol: 43mg 16%

Sodium: 879mg 38%

Saturated Fat: 6g 30%

Total Carbs: 49.1g 16%

Mediterranean Cream Cheese

Serves
5 Persons

Preparation Time
5 min

Ingredients

1 cup cream cheese
½ cup fresh goat's cheese
2 tbsp olive oil
1 tsp freshly squeezed lemon juice
1 tbsp Italian seasoning mix
1 tbsp fresh parsley, finely chopped
¼ tsp chili flakes
1 tsp cumin powder
½ tsp sea salt

Preparation

Combine the ingredients in a blender or a food processor and mix until smooth. Transfer to a glass jar with a tight lid and keep in the refrigerator for up to 7 days.

Total Daily Nutritional Facts

Calories: 257	Protein: 6g	Total Fat: 25.3g 32%	Trans Fat: 0g
Dietary Fiber: 0.1g 0%	Sugars: 0.4g	Cholesterol: 60mg 22%	Sodium: 225mg 10%
Saturated Fat: 13.4g 67%	Total Carbs: 2.5g 1%		

Veal Steak with Mushrooms

Serves
4 Persons

Preparation Time
15 min

Cooking Time
35 min

Ingredients

1 lb veal steaks
1 lb button mushrooms, thinly sliced
3 tbsp olive oil
1 tsp salt
½ tsp freshly ground black pepper
1 bay leaf
1 tbsp dried thyme
7 oz cherry tomatoes

Preparation

Rinse steaks under cold running water and rub with salt, pepper, and thyme. Set aside.

Heat up the olive oil in a large skillet. Add steaks and pour in one cup of water. Bring it to a boil and add one bay leaf. Reduce the heat to medium and simmer until fork tender, for 25 minutes. Add some more water if necessary.

Finally, when all the water has evaporated, add button mushrooms and cherry tomatoes. Give it a good stir and cook for 10 minutes, over medium heat.

Remove from the heat and serve.

Total Daily Nutritional Facts

Calories: 325

Dietary Fiber: 2.1g 7%

Saturated Fat: 4.5g 22%

Protein: 34g

Sugars: 3.3g

Total Carbs: 6.4g 2%

Total Fat: 18.9g 24%

Cholesterol: 120mg 44%

Trans Fat: 0g

Sodium: 700mg 30%

Creamy Asparagus Soup

Serves	Preparation Time	Cooking Time
6 Persons	**15** min	**30 min**

Ingredients

2 lbs fresh wild asparagus, trimmed
2 small onions, peeled and finely chopped
1 cup heavy cream
4 cups vegetable broth
2 tbsp butter
1 tbsp vegetable oil
½ tsp salt
½ tsp dried oregano
½ tsp cayenne pepper

Preparation

Rinse and drain the asparagus. Cut into one-inch long pieces and set aside.

Melt the butter in a large skillet, over medium heat. Add one tablespoon of oil and onions. Stir-fry until translucent.

Now add asparagus, oregano, salt, and cayenne pepper. Stir well and continue to cook until asparagus softens. Transfer to a deep pot. Pour in the vegetable broth and reduce the heat to minimum. Simmer for 20 minutes.

Remove from the heat and stir in heavy cream. Serve immediately.

Total Daily Nutritional Facts

Calories: 189	Protein: 7.3g	Total Fat: 14.7g 19%	Trans Fat: 0g
Dietary Fiber: 3.8g 14%	Sugars: 4.3g	Cholesterol: 38mg 14%	Sodium: 741mg 32%
Saturated Fat: 7.8g 39%	Total Carbs: 9.4g 3%		

Spinach Pie

Serves
4 Persons

Preparation Time
15 min

Cooking Time
35 min

Ingredients

1 lb spinach, rinsed and finely chopped
½ cup of mascarpone cheese
½ cup feta cheese, shredded
3 eggs, beaten
½ cup of goat's cheese
3 tbsp of butter
½ cup of skim milk
½ tsp of salt
1 pack (6 sheets) yufka dough

Preparation

Preheat the oven to 350 degrees.

In a large bowl, combine spinach with eggs, mascarpone, feta, and goat's cheese. Add some salt to taste. Set aside. Dust a clean surface with flour and unfold the sheet of yufka onto it. Using a rolling pin, roll the dough to fit an 8-inches square pan.

Combine milk and butter in a small skillet. Bring it to a boil and allow the butter to melt completely. If needed, add some more salt. Remove from the heat.

Grease the bottom of your baking pan with some oil. Place two yufka sheets and brush with the milk mixture. Make the first layer of spinach mixture and cover with another two yufka sheets. Again, brush with some butter mixture and repeat the process until you have used all the ingredients.

Place in the oven and bake for 35 minutes.

Total Daily Nutritional Facts

Calories: 365

Protein: 14g

Total Fat: 26.8g 34%

Trans Fat: 0g

Dietary Fiber: 2.3g 8%

Sugars: 3.6g

Cholesterol: 149mg 54%

Sodium: 783mg 34%

Saturated Fat: 12.3g 61%

Total Carbs: 18.7g 6%

Boiled Eggs with Spinach and Nuts

2 Persons

10 min   20 min

Ingredients

1 lb fresh spinach, torn
3 tbsp olive oil
2 garlic cloves, crushed
½ tsp sea salt
2 eggs, hard-boiled
5 almonds, finely chopped
5 walnuts, finely chopped
1 tbsp Italian seasoning mix

Preparation

Gently place eggs in a pot of boiling water. Cook for 10-12 minutes. Remove from the heat and drain. Cool to a room temperature and peel. Using a sharp knife, cut eggs in half. Set aside.
Now grease a large skillet with olive oil and heat up over medium-high heat. Add garlic and stir-fry for two minutes.
Now add spinach and continue to cook for five minutes, stirring constantly. Season with Italian seasoning mix, give it a good stir and remove from the heat. Transfer to a serving plate and sprinkle with sea salt, chopped almonds, and walnuts.
Serve with boiled eggs.

Total Daily Nutritional Facts

Calories: 374	Protein: 14.7g	Total Fat: 32.5g 42%	Trans Fat: 0g
Dietary Fiber: 6g 21%	Sugars: 1.5g	Cholesterol: 164mg 60%	Sodium: 779mg 34%
Saturated Fat: 4.9g 24%	Total Carbs: 12.7g 4%		

Black Seafood Risotto with Rosemary

Serves
4 Persons

Preparation Time
15 min

Cooking Time
20 min

Ingredients

1 lb frozen seafood mix
1 cup rice (choose brown rice)
1 tbsp calamari ink
2 tbsp extra virgin olive oil
2 garlic cloves, crushed
1 tbsp finely chopped
rosemary
½ tsp salt

Preparation

Place one cup of rice in a deep pot. Add three cups of water and bring it to a boil. Stir well, reduce the heat and cook for 15 minutes. Stir in calamari ink and remove from the heat. Set aside.

Meanwhile, heat up the olive oil in a medium-sized skillet. Add crushed garlic and rosemary. Stir-fry for 3-4 minutes, stirring constantly. Now add seafood mix and stir well again.

Cook for 15 minutes, or until fork-tender.

Now, stir in rice and serve immediately.

Total Daily Nutritional Facts

Calories: 335	Protein: 19.6g	Total Fat: 8.5g 11%	Trans Fat: 0g
Dietary Fiber: 1g 4%	Sugars: 0.1g	Cholesterol: 116mg 42%	Sodium: 648mg 28%
Saturated Fat: 2.2g 11%	Total Carbs: 40.5g 14%		

Braised Greens with Fresh Mint

Serves	Preparation Time	Cooking Time
4 Persons	**15** min	**20 min**

Ingredients

1 lb fresh chicory, torn
1 lb wild asparagus, finely chopped
7 oz Swiss chard, torn
7 oz arugula, torn
1 cup fresh mint, finely chopped
½ cup rice
3 garlic cloves, crushed
¼ tsp of freshly ground black pepper
1 tsp of salt
¼ cup of freshly squeezed lemon juice
4 tbsp olive oil

Preparation

Place rice in a pot. Add 1 ½ cups of water and bring it to a boil.
Cook for about 10-12 minutes, or until the liquid evaporates. Stir occasionally. Remove from the heat and set aside.
Fill a large pot with salted water and add greens. Bring it to a boil and cook for 2-3 minutes.
Remove from the heat and drain.
In a medium-sized skillet, heat up 3 tablespoons of olive oil. Add crushed garlic and stir-fry for 2-3 minutes. Now add the greens, salt, pepper, and about half of the lemon juice.
Cook for five minutes, stirring constantly.
Finally, add rice and give it a good stir. Remove from the heat and chill to a room temperature.
Drizzle with the remaining lemon juice and serve.

Total Daily Nutritional Facts

Calories: 286	Protein: 8.8g	Total Fat: 15.3g 20%	Trans Fat: 0g
Dietary Fiber: 9.5g 34%	Sugars: 4.4g	Cholesterol: 0mg 0%	Sodium: 740mg 32%
Saturated Fat: 2.3g 12%	Total Carbs: 33.4g 11%		

Blueberry Strudel

Serves	Preparation Time	Cooking Time
8 Persons	**25** min	**35 min**

Ingredients

1 cup fresh blueberries
1 cup fresh raspberries
1 tsp blueberry extract, sugar-free
2 cups Greek yogurt
2 eggs
2 tbsp powdered stevia
2 tbsp unsalted butter, softened
¼ cup cornstarch
2 puff pastry sheets
¼ tsp salt

Preparation

Preheat the oven to 350 degrees. Line some parchment paper over 7x5-inches square baking pan and set aside.

Place blueberries along with stevia, cornstarch, and salt in a food processor. Pulse until smooth and transfer to a heavy-bottomed pot. Add one cup of water and bring it to a boil. Briefly cook for 3 minutes, stirring constantly. Remove from the heat and set aside to cool completely.

In a medium-sized bowl, combine Greek yogurt with blueberry extract. Mix until completely smooth and set aside.

Unfold the pastry and cut each sheet into 4-inch x 7-inch pieces and brush with beaten eggs. Place approximately two tablespoons of cream cheese along with two tablespoons of blueberry mixture at the middle of each pastry. Fold the sheets and brush with the remaining egg mixture. Cut the surface with a sharp knife and gently place each strudel onto a baking sheet.

Bake for 35 minutes.

Total Daily Nutritional Facts

Calories: 162	Protein: 6.3g	Total Fat: 8.5g 11%	Trans Fat: 0g
Dietary Fiber: 1.7g 6%	Sugars: 4.6g	Cholesterol: 10mg 4%	Sodium: 140mg 6%
Saturated Fat: 3.7g 19%	Total Carbs: 15.4g 5%		

Marinated Catfish Fillets

Serves

3 Persons

Preparation Time

40 min

Cooking Time

8 min

Ingredients

1 lb catfish fillet
1 lemon, juiced
½ cup parsley leaves, finely chopped
2 garlic cloves, crushed
1 onion, finely chopped
1 tbsp fresh dill, finely chopped
1 tbsp fresh rosemary
2 cups white wine
2 tbsp Dijon mustard
1 cup extra virgin olive oil

Preparation

In a large bowl, combine lemon juice, parsley leaves, crushed garlic, finely chopped onion, fresh dill, rosemary, white wine, mustard, and olive oil. Stir well to combine. Submerge fillets in this mixture and cover with a tight lid. Refrigerate for 30 minutes (up to two hours).
Preheat a large, non-stick skillet over medium-high heat. Remove the fillets from the refrigerator and drain, but reserve the marinade.
Grill for 4 minutes on each side. Add some of the marinade while grilling to prevent the fillets from sticking.
Remove from the heat and serve immediately.

Total Daily Nutritional Facts

Calories: 495	Protein: 25.4g	Total Fat: 26.3g 34%	Trans Fat: 0g
Dietary Fiber: 2.7g 9%	Sugars: 3.5g	Cholesterol: 71mg 26%	Sodium: 217mg 9%
Saturated Fat: 4.3g 21%	Total Carbs: 12.6g 4%		

Greek Dolmades

Serves
8 Persons

Preparation Time
30 min

Cooking Time
20 min

Ingredients

40 wine leaves, fresh or in jar
1 cup of long grain rice, rinsed
½ cup of olive oil
3 garlic cloves, crushed
¼ cup of freshly squeezed lemon juice
2 tbsp fresh mint
Salt and pepper to taste

Preparation

Wash the leaves thoroughly, one at a time. Place on a clean work surface. Grease the bottom of a deep pot with two tablespoons of olive oil and make a layer with wine leaves. Set aside.

In a medium-sized bowl, combine rice with three tablespoons of olive oil, garlic, mint, salt, and pepper. Place one wine leaf at a time on the work surface and add one teaspoon of filling at the bottom end. Fold the leaf over the filling towards the center. Bring the two sides in towards the center and roll them up tightly. Gently transfer to the pot.

Add the remaining olive oil, 1 cup of water, and lemon juice. Set the heat to medium-low and cook for 20 minutes. Remove from the heat and cool to a room temperature.

Refrigerate for at least one hour before serving.

Total Daily Nutritional Facts

Calories: 197	Protein: 1.8g	Total Fat: 12.8g 16%	Trans Fat: 0g
Dietary Fiber: 0.5g 2%	Sugars: 0.2g	Cholesterol: 0mg 0%	Sodium: 3mg 0%
Saturated Fat: 1.9g 10%	Total Carbs: 19.2g 6%		

Winter Lamb Stew

Serves
4 Persons

Preparation Time
15 min

Cooking Time
1 hr 10 min

Ingredients

1 lb lamb neck, boneless
2 medium-sized potatoes, peeled and chopped into bite-sized pieces
2 large carrots, sliced
1 medium-sized tomato, diced
1 small red bell pepper, chopped
1 garlic head, whole
A handful fresh parsley, finely chopped
2 tbsp extra virgin olive oil
¼ cup lemon juice
1 tsp salt
½ tsp black pepper, ground

Preparation

Grease the bottom of a pressure cooker with olive oil.
Rinse the meat under cold running water and pat dry with a kitchen towel. Rub with salt and place in the cooker along with three cups of water.
Seal the lid and set the steam release handle.
Cook for 30-40 minutes, depending on your cooker. You want the meat half cooked.
Release the pressure and open the cooker. Remove the meat but reserve the liquid.
Transfer the meat into a deep pot along with potatoes, carrots, tomato, bell pepper, garlic head, parsley, lemon juice, pepper, and the remaining salt. Pour in the lamb broth and one more cup of water.
Simmer over medium-high heat for 30-35 minutes, or until potatoes are fork-tender.

Total Daily Nutritional Facts

Calories: 398	Protein: 36g	Total Fat: 15.1g 19%	Trans Fat: 0g
Dietary Fiber: 4.9g 18%	Sugars: 5.8g	Cholesterol: 99mg 36%	Sodium: 700mg 30%
Saturated Fat: 3.9g 19%	Total Carbs: 29.9g 10%		

Berry Waffles

Serves
4 Persons

Preparation Time
10 min

Cooking Time
7-10 min

Ingredients

1 cup all-purpose flour
½ cup buckwheat flour
½ tsp salt
3 eggs
1 tsp vanilla extract,
sugar-free
1 tsp powdered stevia
1 tbsp coconut oil, melted
2 cups skim milk
½ cup blueberry jam

Preparation

Combine the ingredients in a large mixing bowl. Beat well on high speed for 3 minutes. Cook in a waffle iron on medium heat for 7-10 minutes. Top with one tablespoon of blueberry jam. Optionally, *Add some wild berries and serve.*

Total Daily Nutritional Facts

Calories: 389	Protein: 13.5g	Total Fat: 7.5g 10%	Trans Fat: 0g
Dietary Fiber: 2.3g 8%	Sugars: 18.9g	Cholesterol: 125mg 46%	Sodium: 404mg 18%
Saturated Fat: 4.1g 21%	Total Carbs: 66.8g 22%		

Fresh Goat's Cheese Salad

Serves
4 Persons

Preparation Time
15 min

Ingredients

1 large tomato, finely chopped
1 red bell pepper, finely chopped
1 green bell pepper, finely chopped
1 onion, finely chopped
1 cup fresh goat's cheese
2 tbsp extra virgin olive oil
1 tsp Italian seasoning

Preparation

Wash and prepare the vegetables. Place in a large bowl. Stir in fresh goat's cheese and season with Italian seasoning. Drizzle with olive oil and transfer to a serving plate.
Optionally, serve with some kalamata olives and steamed broccoli.

Total Daily Nutritional Facts

Calories: 205

Protein: 7.4g

Total Fat: 16.1g 21%

Trans Fat: 0g

Dietary Fiber: 1.9g 7%

Sugars: 6.2g

Cholesterol: 23mg 8%

Sodium: 151mg 7%

Saturated Fat: 6.9g 35%

Total Carbs: 9.7g 3%

Creme Caramel

Serves
4 Persons

Preparation Time
10 min

Cooking Time
7-10 min

Ingredients

½ cup brown sugar
1 tsp liquid stevia
½ cup water
3 eggs
½ tsp vanilla extract, sugar-free
½ cup skim milk
5 oz whipping cream

Preparation

Preheat the oven to 350 degrees. In a medium-sized saucepan, combine half of the sugar with stevia and water. Heat up over medium heat and cook for 2-3 minutes, or until sugar dissolves. Stir constantly. Now, increase the heat to high and cook for five minutes. Bring it to a boil, or until sugar turns to nice golden brown caramel. Remove from the heat and set aside for 2-3 minutes – until all the bubbles disappear. Pour into small ramekins. Set aside.

In a medium-sized saucepan, combine whipping cream with milk and vanilla extract. Cook for 5-7 minutes, or until small bubbles form. Remove from the heat and set aside.

Using a hand mixer, whisk together eggs and the remaining sugar. Gradually add the cream mixture and whisk until well combined.Now, pour the mixture into small ovenproof ramekins and set aside.

Take a deep baking pan and place the bowls. Pour in about four cups of water and bake for 25-30 minutes, or until set.

Remove from the oven and cool to a room temperature. Transfer to the refrigerator and chill for one hour before serving.

Total Daily Nutritional Facts

Calories: 232

Protein: 5.9g

Total Fat: 14.2g 18%

Trans Fat: 0g

Dietary Fiber: 0g 0%

Sugars: 19.5g

Cholesterol: 168mg 59%

Sodium: 81mg 4%

Saturated Fat: 7.9g 39%

Total Carbs: 20.7g 7%

Fish Stew

Serves	Preparation Time	Cooking Time
8 Persons	**25** min	**17-18** min

Ingredients

1 lb shrimps, whole
1 lb red mullet, cleaned
1 large mackerel, cleaned
1 lb tench fillets
3 large tomatoes, peeled
and roughly chopped
2 onions, finely chopped
2 carrots, grated
2 celery stalks, sliced
3 tbsp olive oil
4 cups fish stock
1 tbsp dried rosemary, finely chopped
1 tsp sea salt

Preparation

Preheat the oil in a large saucepan and add onions, carrots, and celery stalks. Season with salt and rosemary and stir-fry for 5 minutes, until starting to soften. Now add tomatoes and give it a good stir. Continue to cook for 6-7 minutes, stirring occasionally.
Now add fish, scatter over the shrimps, and pour in the fish stock. Bring it to a boil and reduce the heat to medium-low. Cook for 5-7 minutes.

Total Daily Nutritional Facts

Calories: 339	Protein: 42.5g	Total Fat: 14.4g 18%	Trans Fat: 0g
Dietary Fiber: 2g 7%	Sugars: 3.8g	Cholesterol: 168mg 61%	Sodium: 614mg 27%
Saturated Fat: 2.7g 14%	Total Carbs: 8g 3%		

Chocolate Oatmeal with Berries

Serves
2 Persons

Preparation Time
40 min

Ingredients

½ cup rolled oats
½ cup skim milk
2 tbsp Greek yogurt
1 tbsp cocoa powder, unsweetened
1 tsp chia seeds
¼ cup blackberries
¼ cup raspberries
¼ cup cranberries
½ tsp stevia powder
1 tsp vanilla extract, sugar-free

Preparation

In a medium-sized bowl, combine oats with milk. Stir in two tablespoons of Greek yogurt, cocoa powder, vanilla extract, stevia, and chia seeds. Refrigerate for 30 minutes.
Remove from the refrigerator and top with blackberries, raspberries, cranberries, and almonds.

Total Daily Nutritional Facts

Calories: 245	Protein: 10.6g	Total Fat: 9.4g 12%	Trans Fat: 0g
Dietary Fiber: 10.6g 38%	Sugars: 6.3g	Cholesterol: 6mg 2%	Sodium: 40mg 2%
Saturated Fat: 2.1g 10%	Total Carbs: 30.8g 10%		

Vanilla Pudding

Serves	Preparation Time	Cooking Time
2 Persons	**20** min	**10** min

Ingredients

1 cup skim milk
½ cup heavy cream
3 tbsp cornstarch
2 tsp powdered stevia
1 tsp vanilla extract, sugar-free
2 egg yolks
1 tsp coconut oil
1/8 tsp salt
1 pineapple
1 tbsp freshly squeezed lemon juice

Preparation

Cut off the pineapple tops. Using a pineapple corer, remove the inside of the pineapple to create cups. Brush them with freshly squeezed lemon juice and set aside.

In a medium-sized bowl, whisk together milk, heavy cream, and egg yolks. Pour the mixture into the small saucepan. Stir in cornstarch, stevia, and salt. Mix well and heat up over medium-high heat.

Cook for 8-10 minutes, stirring constantly.

Remove from the heat and stir in coconut oil and vanilla extract. Divide the mixture between 2 pineapple cups. Refrigerate for at least one hour before serving.

Optionally, top with some frozen berries and serve.

Total Daily Nutritional Facts

Calories: 276	Protein: 7.4g	Total Fat: 18g 0%	Trans Fat: 0g
Dietary Fiber: 0.1g 1%	Sugars: 6.6g	Cholesterol: 253mg 92%	Sodium: 235mg 10%
Saturated Fat: 0g 0%	Total Carbs: 18.8g 6%		

Thick Okra Soup

Serves	Preparation Time	Cooking Time
5 Persons	25 min	1 hr 15 min

Ingredients

1 lb fresh okra
2 medium-sized tomatoes, roughly chopped
1 large eggplant, sliced into half-inch thick slices
1 small potato, sliced
1 cup cabbage, shredded
2 onions, finely chopped
4 cups beef broth
½ tsp salt
1 tsp cayenne pepper
½ tsp dried thyme
2 bay leaves
¼ tsp freshly ground black pepper
3 tbsp olive oil

Preparation

In a large skillet, heat up the olive oil over medium-high heat. Add onions and stir-fry until translucent. Now add tomatoes, eggplants, and okra. Season with salt, pepper, cayenne pepper, and thyme. Give it a good stir and continue to cook until the tomato liquid evaporates.

Add potato, cabbage, and bay leaf. Pour in the beef broth and bring it to a boil. Reduce the heat to medium-low and simmer for one hour.

Total Daily Nutritional Facts

Calories: 221	Protein: 8.4g	Total Fat: 10.1g 13%	Trans Fat: 0g
Dietary Fiber: 9g 32%	Sugars: 8.6g	Cholesterol: 0mg 0%	Sodium: 860mg 37%
Saturated Fat: 1.6g 8%	Total Carbs: 26.2g 9%		

Grilled Beef Steak

Serves
4 Persons

Preparation Time
1 hr 10 min

Cooking Time
16 min

Ingredients

1 lb flat iron steak
¼ cup Dijon mustard
1 tbsp olive oil
¼ tsp red pepper flakes
1 tbsp fresh rosemary,
finely chopped
½ tsp sea salt

Preparation

Rinse the steak under cold running water. Pat dry with a kitchen paper and set aside.

Whisk together olive oil, Dijon, red pepper flakes, fresh rosemary, and salt. Brush the steak with this mixture and tightly wrap with plastic foil. Refrigerate for one hour.

Preheat the grill to medium-high. Remove the steak from the refrigerator and slice into one-inch thick slices.

Grill steak for 8 minutes on one side. Flim and grill for 8 more minutes for medium-rare.

Total Daily Nutritional Facts

Calories: 313	Protein: 36.2g	Total Fat: 17.5g 22%	Trans Fat: 0g
Dietary Fiber: 0.9g 3%	Sugars: 0.1g	Cholesterol: 97mg 35%	Sodium: 492mg 21%
Saturated Fat: 5.8g 29%	Total Carbs: 1.4g 0%		

Moroccan Breakfast Salad

Serves

3 Persons

Preparation Time

20 min

Ingredients

1 medium-sized pear, sliced
1 kiwi, peeled and sliced
5 cherry tomatoes, halved
½ green bell pepper, sliced
¼ cup blackberries
¼ cup raspberries
¼ cup blueberries
¼ cup peanuts, unsalted
5 almonds, toasted
For the dressing:
2 tbsp honey
¼ cup freshly squeezed lime juice
1 tbsp Dijon mustard

Preparation

Whisk together honey, Dijon, and lime juice. Set aside. Combine the salad ingredients in a large bowl. Drizzle with honey mixture and toss to combine.
Refrigerate for 30 minutes before serving.

Total Daily Nutritional Facts

Calories: 230	Protein: 6.7g	Total Fat: 8g 10%	Trans Fat: 0g
Dietary Fiber: 8g 29%	Sugars: 27.6g	Cholesterol: 0mg 0%	Sodium: 74mg 3%
Saturated Fat: 1g 5%	Total Carbs: 38.9g 13%		

Seafood Pasta with Fresh Parsley

Serves	Preparation Time	Cooking Time
5 Persons	15 min	20 min

Ingredients

1 lb linguine pasta
7 oz frozen seafood mix, defrosted
3 tbsp olive oil
2 garlic cloves, crushed
1 large onion, finely chopped
3 cups chicken stock
½ tsp of dried oregano
¼ tsp of salt
¼ cup of white wine
¼ cup fresh parsley leaves, finely chopped

Preparation

Heat up the olive oil in a large, non-stick skillet. Add onions, garlic, and stir-fry until translucent.
Now add seafood and season with salt and oregano. Reduce the heat to minimum and simmer for 10 minutes, stirring occasionally. Add chicken stock, white wine, and pasta. Give it a good stir and cook for 7 minutes, or until tender. Remove from the heat and sprinkle with fresh parsley.Optionally stir in one cup of homemade tomato sauce before serving. You'll need:
3 large ripe tomatoes, roughly chopped
¼ cup tomato paste
1 tbsp brown sugar
½ tsp sea salt
2 tbsp extra virgin olive oil
1 tsp ground cumin
Heat up the oil over medium-high heat. Add tomatoes, tomato paste, sugar, salt, and cumin. Reduce the heat to low and simmer until completely softened. Transfer to glass jars with tight lids and keep in the refrigerator up to one week.

Total Daily Nutritional Facts

Calories: 385	Protein: 15g	Saturated Fat: 1.4g 7%	Trans Fat: 0g
Total Fat: 9g 12%	Sugars: 2.9g	Cholesterol: 34mg 12%	Sodium: 585mg 25%
Dietary Fiber: 3.4g 12%	Total Carbs: 61g 20%		

Ground Beef Kebab

Serves
4 Persons

Preparation Time
25 min

Cooking Time
6-7 min

Ingredients

1 lb ground beef
1 onion, finely chopped
2 garlic cloves, crushed
½ tsp salt
¼ tsp freshly ground black pepper
1 tsp bicarbonate of soda
¼ cup water

Preparation

Preheat the grill over medium-high heat. In a large bowl, combine beef with finely chopped onion, garlic, salt, pepper, bicarbonate of soda, and water. Mix well until completely combined.
Shape the mixture into 20 equal balls. Roll each into a long (3- inches long and half-inch thick).
Grill kebabs for 3-4 minutes. Flip and grill for another 2-3 minutes.
Serve immediately.

Total Daily Nutritional Facts

Calories: 224	Protein: 34.8g	Total Fat: 7.1g 9%	Trans Fat: 0g
Dietary Fiber: 0.7g 2%	Sugars: 1.2g	Cholesterol: 101mg 37%	Sodium: 682mg 30%
Saturated Fat: 2.7g 13%	Total Carbs: 3.2g 1%		

Vanilla French Toast

Serves
3 Persons

Preparation Time
10 min

Cooking Time
5 min

Ingredients

6 slices toast bread, choose whole grain
2 eggs
½ cup skim milk
1 tsp vanilla extract, sugar-free
½ tsp cinnamon
1 tbsp coconut oil, melted
1 tsp powdered stevia, optional

Preparation

Grease a large skillet with some coconut oil.
Whisk together eggs, milk, vanilla extract, and cinnamon. Submerge toast in this mixture and place in the skillet. Cook for 2 minutes on one side, gently flip it and continue to cook for 1-2 minutes more. Remove from the heat and optionally sprinkle with some powdered stevia.

Total Daily Nutritional Facts

Calories: 239	Protein: 9.7g	Total Fat: 9.7g 12%	Trans Fat: 0g
Dietary Fiber: 4.1g 15%	Sugars: 5.8g	Cholesterol: 110mg 40%	Sodium: 282mg 12%
Saturated Fat: 5.3g 26%	Total Carbs: 25.3g 8%		

Pasta Bolognese

Serves
6 Persons

Preparation Time
20 min

Cooking Time
40 min

Ingredients

14 oz Penne Rigate

7 oz lean ground beef

2 medium-sized onions, peeled and finely chopped

1 large tomato, peeled and roughly chopped

1 tbsp tomato paste

½ tsp dried oregano

¼ cup white wine

1 tsp powdered stevia

1 tsp sea salt

1 tbsp extra virgin olive oil

Parmesan cheese, optional

Fresh parsley, optional

Preparation

Place pasta in a deep, heavy-bottomed pot. Add enough water to cover and bring it to a boil. Cook for 10-12 minutes, or until soft.

Remove from the heat and drain. Set aside. Grease a large skillet with one tablespoon of olive oil and heat up over medium-high heat. Add onions and stir-fry until translucent. Now add chopped tomato, tomato paste, salt, stevia, and oregano. Continue to cook for ten minutes, or until the liquid evaporates. Finally, add ground beef and white wine. Give it a good stir and reduce the heat to medium-low. Cook for 15 minutes, stirring occasionally.

Stir in cooked pasta and mix well. Optionally, sprinkle with some fresh parsley or grated Parmesan. Serve warm.

Total Daily Nutritional Facts

Calories: 350	Protein: 18.6g	Total Fat: 5.7g 7%	Trans Fat: 0g
Dietary Fiber: 3.7g 13%	Sugars: 6.3g	Cholesterol: 30mg 11%	Sodium: 340mg 15%
Saturated Fat: 1.4g 7%	Total Carbs: 54.5g 18%		

Braised Swiss Chard

Serves
4 Persons

Preparation Time
25 min

Cooking Time
6-7 min

Ingredients

1 lb of Swiss chard, torn (keep the stems)
1 medium-sized potato, peeled and finely chopped
¼ cup of extra virgin olive oil
1 tsp garlic powder
½ tsp sea salt

Preparation

Rinse thoroughly the Swiss chard and drain in a large colander. Using a sharp knife, cut into bite-sized pieces. Place in a deep pot and pour in enough water to cover. Briefly boil, for 2 minutes and remove from the heat. Drain and set aside.

In a large skillet, heat up the olive oil over medium-high heat. Add finely chopped potatoes and about ½ cup of water. Cook over medium heat until fork-tender.

Stir in Swiss chard and season with salt and garlic. Give it a good stir and cook for 5 minutes.

Total Daily Nutritional Facts

Calories: 347	Protein: 6.5g	Total Fat: 25.9g 33%,	Trans Fat: 0g
Dietary Fiber: 6.3g 22%	Sugars: 3.7g	Cholesterol: 0mg 0%	Sodium: 960mg 42%
Saturated Fat: 3.6g 18%,	Total Carbs: 28.1g 9%		

Goat's Cheese Omelet

Serves
2 Persons

Preparation Time
5 min

Cooking Time
5 min

Ingredients

3 eggs
2 tbsp extra-virgin olive oil
2 tbsp goat's cheese, crumbled
½ tsp turmeric, ground
½ tsp sea salt
½ tsp freshly ground black pepper

Preparation

Whisk together eggs and goat's cheese. Season with salt, pepper, and ground turmeric.
Grease a small, non-stick pan with olive oil and heat up over medium-high heat. Pour in the egg mixture and tilt the pan to spread evenly. Cook for 2 minutes.
Using a kitchen spatula, ease around the edges and fold it over in half.
Serve immediately.

Total Daily Nutritional Facts

Calories: 269	Protein: 11.5g	Total Fat: 24.9g 32%	Trans Fat: 0g
Dietary Fiber: 0.3g 1%	Sugars: 0.9g	Cholesterol: 257mg 93%	Sodium: 634mg 28%
Saturated Fat: 7g 35%	Total Carbs: 1.6g 1%		

Berry Cake

15 Persons   60 min   30 min

Ingredients

For the crust:
1 lb all-purpose flour
1 lb brown sugar
2 tsp vanilla extract, sugar-free
½ tsp salt
1 tsp baking powder

For the chocolate topping:
2 cups whipping cream
1 cup heavy cream
¼ cup cocoa powder, unsweetened
¼ cup powdered stevia

For the berry topping:
1 lb fresh cranberries
2 tbsp gelatin
2 tbsp powdered stevia

Preparation

Preheat the oven to 450 degrees. Line 9x5 inches square pan with some parchment paper and set aside. First, you will have to prepare the crust. Combine eggs, sugar, and vanilla extract in a large mixing bowl. Beat well on high speed until light and fluffy.
In another bowl, combine flour with salt and baking powder. Mix well and add sugar mixture. Beat well again for 3 minutes on high speed. If the dough is too thick, add two tablespoons of water.
Transfer the dough to a baking dish and bake for 10 minutes. Remove from the oven and cool to a room temperature.
Meanwhile, prepare the filling. In a large mixing bowl, combine whipping cream with heavy cream, cocoa powder, and stevia. Beat on high speed until smooth. Pour the mixture over the crust and refrigerate for at least 30 minutes.
Now prepare the final layer. Place cranberries in a deep pot. Pour in 2 cups of water and add stevia. Bring it to a boil and reduce the heat to low. Simmer for 20 minutes. Finally, add gelatin and give it a good stir. Continue to cook until thick. Remove from the heat and pour over the cake. Cool completely before serving.

Total Daily Nutritional Facts

Calories: 321	Protein: 3.9g	Sugars: 30.7g	Dietary Fiber: 2.4g 8%
Trans Fat: 0g	Total Carbs: 57.2g 19%	Saturated Fat: 5.1g 25%	Cholesterol: 29mg 10%
Total Fat: 8.4g 11%	Sodium: 96mg 4%		

Stuffed Onions

Serves
6 Persons

Preparation Time
30 min

Cooking Time
60 min

Ingredients

10-12 medium-sized onions, peeled
1 lb lean ground beef
½ cup brown rice
3 tbsp olive oil
1 tbsp dried mint, ground
1 tsp Cayenne pepper, ground
½ tsp cumin powder
1 tsp salt
½ cup tomato paste
½ cup Italian-style breadcrumbs

Preparation

Cut a ¼-inch slice from top of each onion and trim a small amount from the bottom end, This will make the onions stand upright. Place onions in a microwave-safe dish and add about one cup of water.

Cover with a tight lid and microwave on high 10 to 12 minutes or until onions are tender. Remove onions from a dish and cool slightly.

Now carefully remove inner layers of onions with a paring knife, leaving about a ¼-inch onion shell.

In a large bowl, combine ground beef with rice, olive oil, mint, cayenne pepper, cumin, salt, and bread crumbs. Use one tablespoon of the mixture to fill the onions.

Grease the bottom of a deep pot with olive oil and add onions. Pour in about two cups of water and cover. Simmer over medium heat for 45 minutes.

Total Daily Nutritional Facts

Calories: 250	Protein: 18.3g	Total Fat: 11.8g 15%	Trans Fat: 0g
Dietary Fiber: 2.2g 8%	Sugars: 5.7g	Cholesterol: 46mg 17%	Sodium: 605mg 26%
Saturated Fat: 3g 15%	Total Carbs: 18.9g 6%		

Grilled Beef Liver

Serves
4 Persons

Preparation Time
35 min

Cooking Time
5 min

Ingredients

1 lb beef liver, cut into thin slices
3 tbsp olive oil
2 garlic cloves, crushed
1 tbsp fresh mint, finely chopped
½ tbsp cayenne pepper, ground
1 tsp salt
½ tsp Italian seasoning

Preparation

Preheat a large grill pan over medium-high heat.
Rinse the liver thoroughly under cold running water. Make sure to wash out all the blood traces. Pat dry with a kitchen paper. Using a sharp knife, remove all tough veins, if any. Cut crosswise into thin slices. In a small bowl, combine olive oil, garlic, mint, cayenne, salt and Italian seasoning. Mix until well incorporated. Generously brush the liver slices with this mixture and grill for 3-4 minutes on each side.

Total Daily Nutritional Facts

Calories: 295	Protein: 30.3g	Total Fat: 16.1g 21%	Trans Fat: 0g
Dietary Fiber: 0.3g 1%	Sugars: 0.1g	Cholesterol: 432mg 157%	Sodium: 670mg 29%
Saturated Fat: 3.2g 16%	Total Carbs: 6.9g 2%		

Baked Avocado Eggs

Serves
2 Persons

Preparation Time
10 min

Cooking Time
15 min

Ingredients

1 avocado, halved and pitted
2 eggs
1 tbsp Italian seasoning
¼ tsp red pepper flakes

Preparation

Preheat the oven to 400 degrees. Line a small square baking pan with some parchment paper and set aside. Cut avocado in half and remove the pit. Place avocado halves in a baking pan. Slowly pour the eggs into each hole and sprinkle with Italian seasoning and red pepper flakes.
Bake for 15 minutes.

Total Daily Nutritional Facts

Calories: 290	Protein: 7.5g	Total Fat: 26.1g 33%	Trans Fat: 0g
Dietary Fiber: 6.8g 24%	Sugars: 1.5g	Cholesterol: 169mg 61%	Sodium: 70mg 3%
Saturated Fat: 5.8g 29%	Total Carbs: 9.9g 3%		

Braised Leeks with Beef

Serves
4 Persons

Preparation Time
20 min

Cooking Time
60 min

Ingredients

6 large leeks
1 lb beef stew meat
1 bay leaf
1 medium-sized carrot, sliced
1 cup fresh celery leaves, chopped
1 small onion, sliced
1 tsp salt
¼ tsp freshly ground black pepper
3 tbsp of extra virgin olive oil
2 tbsp of vegetable oil
¼ cup of white wine
½ tsp of dry rosemary

Preparation

Grease the bottom of your pressure cooker with 2 tablespoons of vegetable oil. Generously sprinkle the meat with salt and place in your cooker.
Add onions, carrots, celery, and bay leaf. Pour in enough water to cover and close the lid.
Set the steam release handle and cook for 45 minutes (or less depending on the type of your pressure cooker).
Release the steam and open the lid. Set aside.
Rinse the leeks and cut into bite-sized pieces. In a large skillet, heat up the olive oil over medium-high heat. Add leeks and stir-fry for 10 minutes. Transfer to a deep pot. Add the meat along with carrots and onions, wine, and rosemary. Give it a good stir and bring it to a boil.
Cook for five more minutes, stirring constantly.

Total Daily Nutritional Facts

Calories: 473

Protein: 36.9g

Total Fat: 24.9g 32%

Trans Fat: 0g

Dietary Fiber: 3.7g 13%

Sugars: 7.2g

Cholesterol: 101g 37%

Sodium: 715mg 31%

Saturated Fat: 5.6g 28

Total Carbs: 23.5g 8%

Collard Greens with Shrimps

Serves	Preparation Time	Cooking Time
4 Persons	**30** min	**60 min**

Ingredients

2 lbs collard greens, chopped
1 lb shrimps, whole
1 lb octopus
1 large tomato, peeled and finely chopped
3 cups fish stock
2 tbsp extra virgin olive oil
3 garlic cloves
2 tbsp fresh parsley, finely chopped
1 tsp sea salt

Preparation

Rinse well the greens and drain in a large colander.
Place on a clean working surface and chop with a sharp knife. Set aside.
Place octopus in your pressure cooker. Add enough water to cover and cook for 45 minutes (or less, depending on your pressure cooker).
When done, remove from the cooker and cool for a while. Using a sharp knife, cut into bite-sized pieces. Set aside. Meanwhile, rinse the shrimps and place in a deep pot. Add chopped octopus, tomato, and fish stock. Bring it to a boil and cook for 5-7 minutes. Remove from the heat and drain. Set aside. Grease a large, non-stick skillet with olive oil and add garlic. Stir-fry until translucent. Add collard greens and cook for 5 minutes, stirring constantly.
Finally, add shrimps, octopus, parsley, and salt. Give it a good stir and cook for 3 more minutes.
Remove from the heat and serve.

Total Daily Nutritional Facts

Calories: 393	Protein: 54.7g	Total Fat: 13.2g 17%	Trans Fat: 0g
Dietary Fiber: 8.1g 29%	Sugars: 1.2g	Cholesterol: 241mg 87%	Sodium: 1058mg 46%
Saturated Fat: 2g 10%	Total Carbs: 16.8g 6%		

Spinach Omelet with Kefir

Serves
2 Persons

Preparation Time
5 min

Cooking Time
12-15 min

Ingredients

2 eggs
2 cups fresh spinach, finely chopped
1 cup of kefir
2 tbsp olive oil
½ tsp sea salt
3 tbsp grated Ricotta, optional

Preparation

Grease a large skillet with olive oil and add spinach. Cook for 5 minutes over medium heat, stirring constantly. Remove from the heat and transfer to a food processor along with kefir. Blend for one minute and set aside.

Place a medium-sized, non-stick pan on medium-high heat. Crack the eggs and season with salt. Beat well with a fork and pour into the pan. Cook until set, for 2-3 minutes.

Remove from the heat and slide onto a plate. Add spinach mixture and fold it over in half.

Optionally, sprinkle the omelet with some grated Ricotta.

Total Daily Nutritional Facts

Calories: 303	Protein: 13.1g	Total Fat: 24.3g 31%	Trans Fat: 0g
Dietary Fiber: 2.2g 8%	Sugars: 6.5g	Cholesterol: 186mg 68%	Sodium: 645mg 28%
Saturated Fat: 7g 35%	Total Carbs: 10.1g 3%		

Chocolate Smoothie

Serves
1 Persons

Preparation Time
5 min

Ingredients

½ cup skim milk
½ cup coconut water
2 tbsp Greek yogurt
1 tbsp cocoa powder,
unsweetened
1 tsp powdered stevia
1 tsp vanilla extract

Preparation

Combine the ingredients in a blender and pulse until smooth.
Serve immediately.

Total Daily Nutritional Facts

Calories: 118	Protein: 9.4g	Total Fat: 1.7g 2%	Trans Fat: 0g
Dietary Fiber: 2.9g 10%	Sugars: 11.2g	Cholesterol: 4mg 2%	Sodium: 204mg 9%
Saturated Fat: 1.2g 6%	Total Carbs: 15.4g 5%		

Cold Green Bean Salad with Fresh Lime

Serves
2 Persons

Preparation Time
15 min

Cooking Time
30-35 min

Ingredients

1 lb fresh green beans, trimmed
¼ cup extra virgin olive oil
1 tbsp of Dijon mustard
2 garlic cloves, crushed
1 tbsp of lime juice

Preparation

Wash and trim the beans. Place in a deep pot and add enough water to cover. Bring it to a boil and cook until fork tender, for 15-20 minutes. Remove the beans from the heat and drain in a large colander.

Grease a large skillet with some oil and add garlic. Stir-fry until translucent. Now add beans and the remaining oil. Stir in Dijon and lime juice. Give it a good stir and cook for five more minutes, stirring constantly.

Remove from the heat and cool completely. Keep in the refrigerator for 20-30 minutes before serving.

Total Daily Nutritional Facts

Calories: 297

Protein: 4.7g

Total Fat: 25.8g 33%

Trans Fat: 0g

Dietary Fiber: 28g 29%

Sugars: 3.3g

Cholesterol: 0mg 0%

Sodium: 103mg 4%

Saturated Fat: 3.7g 18%

Total Carbs: 17.8g 6%

Red Lentil Soup

Serves
4 Persons

Preparation Time
10 min

Cooking Time
30 min

Ingredients

1 cup of red lentils, soaked
1 medium-sized onion,
peeled and finely chopped
½ cup of sweet carrot puree
1 tbsp of all-purpose flour
½ tsp of freshly ground black
pepper
½ tsp of cumin, ground
½ tsp of salt
2 tbsp of olive oil
4 cups vegetable stock

Preparation

Grease the bottom of a deep pot with olive oil and add onions. Stir-fry for 3 minutes, or until translucent. Stir in flour and continue to cook for one more minute.
Now add lentils and carrot puree. Give it a good stir and continue to cook for 2 more minutes. Pour in the vegetable broth and season with salt, pepper, and cumin.
Bring it to a boil and reduce the heat to medium-low. Simmer for 25 minutes.

Total Daily Nutritional Facts

Calories: 265	Protein: 13.6g	Total Fat: 7.7g 10%	Trans Fat: 0g
Dietary Fiber: 15.9g 57	Sugars: 4.4g	Cholesterol: 0mg 0%	Sodium: 367mg 16%
Saturated Fat: 1.1g 5%	Total Carbs: 36.2g 12%		

Wild Salmon with Spinach

Serves
3 Persons

Preparation Time
15 min

Cooking Time
25 min

Ingredients

1 lb wild salmon fillet, boneless
1 lb fresh spinach, torn
2 tbsp olive oil
2 garlic cloves, finely chopped
2 tbsp lemon juice
1 tbsp fresh rosemary, chopped
1 tsp sea salt

Preparation

Preheat the oven to 400 degrees.
Rinse the fillet under cold running water and rub with salt and rosemary. Place onto a lightly greased baking sheet and bake for 25 minutes.
Meanwhile, heat up the olive oil in a large skillet. Add garlic and stir-fry for 2-3 minutes. Add spinach and continue to cook for 5-7 minutes, stirring constantly. Remove from the heat and sprinkle with fresh lemon juice.
Serve with baked salmon.

Total Daily Nutritional Facts

Calories: 284	Protein: 32.6g	Total Fat: 14.9g 19%	Trans Fat: 0g
Dietary Fiber: 3.9g 14%	Sugars: 0.9g	Cholesterol: 0mg 0%	Sodium: 1093mg 48%
Saturated Fat: 2.9g 15%	Total Carbs: 7.1g 2%		

Easy Chicken Wraps

Serves
4 Persons

Preparation Time
15 min

Cooking Time
20 min

Ingredients

7 oz chicken breast, boneless and skinless
1 medium-sized red bell pepper
½ cup red kidney beans, pre-cooked
1 small cucumber, sliced
2 tbsp olive oil
1 tbsp Italian seasoning
4 whole wheat tortillas

Preparation

Grease a large, non-stick skillet with olive oil. Add chicken breast and cook over medium heat for 20 minutes, stirring occasionally. Remove from the heat and soak the excess oil with some kitchen paper. Sprinkle tortillas with some water and microwave for 1 minute each. Place some of the meat and vegetables at the center of each tortilla. Season with Italian seasoning and wrap. Secure with some toothpicks and serve.

Total Daily Nutritional Facts

Calories: 336	Protein: 20.5g	Total Fat: 10.7g 14%	Trans Fat: 0g
Dietary Fiber: 7.3g 26%	Sugars: 3.6g	Cholesterol: 34mg 12%	Sodium: 161mg 7%
Saturated Fat: 1.2g 6%	Total Carbs: 41.5g 14%		

Mediterranean Scallops

Serves
2 Persons

Preparation Time
5 min

Cooking Time
20 min

Ingredients

4 large Mediterranean scallops, cleaned
2 tbsp extra virgin olive oil
1 tsp sea salt
1 tsp garlic powder
1 tbsp freshly squeezed lemon juice
1 tsp dried rosemary
1 cup white wine

Preparation

Rinse well scallops under cold running water. Place in a heavy-bottomed pot and pour in white wine, rosemary, lemon juice, garlic powder, salt, and olive oil. Add one cup of water and bring it to a boil. Cook until barely tender, 3-4 minutes. Reduce the heat to medium and simmer for ten more minutes.
Remove from the heat and chill for a while. Place each scallop on a serving plate and brush with the remaining liquid.
Serve with grilled asparagus.

Total Daily Nutritional Facts

Calories: 279

Dietary Fiber: 0.4g 2%

Saturated Fat: 2.2g 11%

Protein: 10.5g

Sugars: 6.2g

Total Carbs: 6.2g 2%

Total Fat: 14.6g 19%

Cholesterol: 20mg 7%

Trans Fat: 0g

Sodium: 1041mg 45%

Garlic Meatballs

Serves
5 Persons

Preparation Time
20 min

Cooking Time
15 min

Ingredients

1 lb lean ground beef
¼ cup rice
2 small onions, peeled and finely chopped
2 garlic cloves, crushed
1 egg, beaten
1 large potato, peeled and sliced
1 tbsp tomato paste
3 tbsp of extra virgin olive oil
1 tsp of salt

Preparation

In a large bowl, combine meat with rice, garlic, egg, and salt. Stir well and shape into 15-20 bite-sized meatballs. Heat up the oil in a large skillet. Add onions and stir-fry until translucent. Stir in tomato paste and potato. Continue to cook for 4-5 minutes, stirring constantly.
Reduce the heat to low and add meatballs. Pour in one cup of water and simmer for 40 minutes.

Total Daily Nutritional Facts

Calories: 338	Protein: 21.9g	Total Fat: 16g 20%	Trans Fat: 0g
Dietary Fiber: 2.4g 9%	Sugars: 2.2g	Cholesterol: 89mg 33%	Sodium: 555mg 24%
Saturated Fat: 3.9g 20%	Total Carbs: 28g 9%		

Eggs Stuffed with Shrimps Avocado and Spices

Serves
2 Persons

Preparation Time
15 min

Cooking Time
14 min

Ingredients

2 eggs
4 small shrimps
1 tbsp Dijon mustard
¼ tsp freshly ground black pepper
½ medium-sized avocado, halved
1 tbsp dried oregano
2 tbsp olive oil
¼ cup freshly squeezed lemon juice

Preparation

Grease a medium-sized skillet with olive oil and add shrimps. Cook for 3-4 minutes, turning occasionally. Remove from the heat and set aside.

Gently place two eggs in a pot of boiling water. You can add one teaspoon of baking soda – this will make the peeling process much easier. Cook for 10 minutes. Remove from the heat and drain. Chill for a while. Slice the eggs in half and remove the yolk. Set aside.

In a medium-sized bowl, combine the egg yolks with avocado, mustard, black pepper, and lemon juice. Transfer to a blender and pulse to combine. Use this mixture to stuff each egg. Top with shrimp and sprinkle with oregano.

Total Daily Nutritional Facts

Calories: 356	Protein: 17g	Total Fat: 29.7g 38%	Trans Fat: 0g
Dietary Fiber: 4.8g 17%	Sugars: 1.4g	Cholesterol: 253mg 92%	Sodium: 264mg 11%
Saturated Fat: 6g 30%	Total Carbs: 8g 3%		

Funghi Pizza

Serves
5 Persons

Preparation Time
20 min

Cooking Time
15 min

Ingredients

¾ cup all-purpose flour
1 cup whole wheat flour
½ tsp brown sugar
2 tsp dried yeast
¼ tsp salt
1 tbsp olive oil
1 cup lukewarm water
1 cup button mushrooms, sliced
¼ cup Gouda, grated
2 tbsp tomato paste, sugar-free
½ tsp dried oregano
¼ cup lukewarm water

Preparation

In a large mixing bowl fitted with a dough hook attachment, combine all-purpose flour with whole wheat flour, brown sugar, dried yeast, and salt. Mix well and gradually add lukewarm water and oil. Continue to beat on high speed until smooth dough.
Transfer to a lightly floured surface and knead until completely smooth. Form into a tight ball and wrap tightly in plastic foil. Set aside for one hour.
Preheat the oven to 400 degrees. Line some parchment paper over a round baking pan and set aside.
Roll out the dough with a rolling pin and transfer to a baking dish. Brush with tomato paste and sprinkle with oregano, gouda, and button mushroom.
Bake for 15-20 minutes.

Total Daily Nutritional Facts

Calories: 278	Protein: 8.4g	Total Fat: 4.5g 6%	Trans Fat: 0g
Dietary Fiber: 42.9g 10%	Sugars: 2.8g	Cholesterol: 2mg 1%	Sodium: 172mg 7%
Saturated Fat: 0.9g 4%	Total Carbs: 50.2g 17%		

Orange Baked Whiting

Serves
4 Persons

Preparation Time
10 min

Cooking Time
20 min

Ingredients

2 lbs fresh whiting (can be replaced with frozen), cleaned
2 tbsp honey
¼ cup freshly squeezed orange juice
1 tbsp orange zest
1 large orange, sliced
½ tsp sea salt
1 tsp dried thyme

Preparation

Preheat the oven to 400 degrees.
Rinse the fish and pat dry with a kitchen paper.
Whisk together honey, orange juice, orange zest, salt, and thyme. Brush the mixture over fish and place in a baking dish lined with some parchment paper. Add orange slices and bake for 15-20 minutes.
Serve warm.

Total Daily Nutritional Facts

Calories: 360

Protein: 51.9g

Total Fat: 8.2g 11%

Trans Fat: 0g

Dietary Fiber: 1.4g 5%

Sugars: 14.2g

Cholesterol: 189mg 69%

Sodium: 491mg 21%

Saturated Fat: 1.4g 7%

Total Carbs: 16.2g 5%

Poached Eggs with Garlic and Leeks

Serves
2 Persons

Preparation Time
5 min

Cooking Time
13 min

Ingredients

1 lb fresh leeks, chopped into bite-sized pieces
1 cup fresh spinach, finely chopped
1 cup Swiss chard, torn
7-8 garlic cloves, whole
2 tbsp olive oil
4 large eggs
½ tsp salt

Preparation

Heat up the olive oil over medium-high heat. Add garlic and stir-fry for three minutes. Now add leeks, spinach, and chard. Continue to cook for 4-5 minutes, stirring constantly.
Gently crack the eggs and season with salt. Cook until set, for 2-3 minutes.

Total Daily Nutritional Facts

Calories: 283	Protein: 11.6g	Total Fat: 16.5g 21%	Trans Fat: 0g
Dietary Fiber: 3.3g 12%	Sugars: 6.7g	Cholesterol: 248mg 90%	Sodium: 546mg 24%
Saturated Fat: 3.5g 17%	Total Carbs: 25g 8%		

Classic Churros with Lemon

Serves
8 Persons

Preparation Time
15 min

Cooking Time
15 min

Ingredients

1 cup all-purpose flour
1 cup water
1/3 cup brown sugar
1/3 cup coconut oil
3 eggs
¼ tsp salt
¼ cup freshly
squeezed lemon juice
1 tsp lemon extract
Oil for frying

Preparation

In a large mixing bowl, combine all dry ingredients and stir well. Gradually add water and coconut oil, beating constantly. Finally, add eggs, one at the time. Beat well on high speed for 3 minutes or until smooth dough. Transfer into a large piping bag with a star tip.
Heat up some oil over medium-high heat. Pipe 2-inches long churros into a frying pan and cook for 3-4 minutes, or until golden brown color.
Drain on a kitchen paper and chill to a room temperature. Transfer to the refrigerator to cool completely.

Total Daily Nutritional Facts

Calories: 185	Protein: 3.8g	Total Fat: 10.9g 14%	Trans Fat: 0g
Dietary Fiber: 0.5g 2%	Sugars: 6.3g	Cholesterol: 61mg 61%	Sodium: 101mg 4%
Saturated Fat: 8.4g 42%	Total Carbs: 18.2g 6%		

Spring Spinach Soup

Serves
4 Persons

Preparation Time
15 min

Cooking Time
28 min

Ingredients

1 lb lamb rack
1 lb spinach, torn
3 large leeks, chopped into bite-sized pieces
2 tbsp olive oil
2 garlic cloves
½ tsp salt

Preparation

Rinse the meat and rub with salt. Place in the pressure cooker and pour in enough water to cover. Seal the lid and cook until tender, depending on your pressure cooker. Release the steam and open the lid. Remove the meat and keep the liquid. Set aside.

Grease a deep pot with olive oil and heat up over medium-high heat. Add garlic and stir-fry for 2-3 minutes. Add spinach and leeks and continue to cook for 3 minutes.

Now add the meat and pour in the broth. Bring it to a boil and cook for 3-4 minutes.

Serve immediately.

Total Daily Nutritional Facts

Calories: 320	Protein: 27.4g	Total Fat: 17.7g 23%	Trans Fat: 0g
Dietary Fiber: 3.7g 13%	Sugars: 3.1g	Cholesterol: 75mg 27%	Sodium: 474mg 21%
Saturated Fat: 4.6g 23%	Total Carbs: 14.1g 5%		

Wild Asparagus with Tuna and Garlic

Serves
2 Persons

Preparation Time
5 min

Cooking Time
3 min

Ingredients

10 oz wild asparagus
1 cup canned tuna, oil-free and drained
2 cloves of garlic, sliced
2 tbsp olive oil
1 tbsp Italian seasoning

Preparation

Rinse well the asparagus and drain in a large colander. Cut into bite-sized pieces and set aside.
Grease a large skillet with olive oil. Add garlic and stir-fry for 2-3 minutes. Season with Italian seasoning and add asparagus. Continue to cook for 5 minutes, stirring constantly.
Remove from the heat and cool to a room temperature. Transfer to a serving plate and top with tuna.

Total Daily Nutritional Facts

Calories: 287	Protein: 23.9g	Total Fat: 19g 24%	Trans Fat: 0g
Dietary Fiber: 2.9g 10%	Sugars: 2.5g	Cholesterol: 41mg 15%	Sodium: 347mg 15%
Saturated Fat: 3.1g 15%	Total Carbs: 7.6g 3%		

Blueberry Greek Yogurt with Bananas

Serves
2 Persons

Preparation Time
40 min

Ingredients

1 cup Greek yogurt
1 ½ banana
1 tsp blueberry extract
1 tsp powdered stevia
1 tbsp chia seeds
4 walnuts, finely chopped
3 almonds

Preparation

Combine Greek yogurt, one banana, blueberry extract, and stevia in a blender. Pulse until smooth. Transfer to a serving bowl and freeze for 30 minutes.

Top with the remaining banana, chia seeds, walnuts, and almonds. Optionally, add some berries and blueberry jam.

Total Daily Nutritional Facts

Calories: 291	Protein: 15.9g	Total Fat: 15g 19%	Trans Fat: 0g
Dietary Fiber: 8.2g 29%	Sugars: 15.2g	Cholesterol: 5mg 2%	Sodium: 34mg 1%
Saturated Fat: 2.7g 14%	Total Carbs: 32g 11%		

Oven Baked Sea Bream

Serves
4 Persons

Preparation Time
15 min

Cooking Time
20 min

Ingredients

2 sea bream
(about 1 lb each), gutted and cleaned
4 tbsp olive oil
¼ cup white wine
2 tbsp freshly squeezed lemon juice
1 tbsp dried rosemary
½ tsp sea salt
¼ tsp red pepper flakes

Preparation

Preheat the oven to 400 degrees. Line some parchment paper over a baking sheet and set aside.
In a medium-sized bowl, whisk together olive oil, wine, lemon juice, salt, and pepper flakes. Generously brush the fish with this mixture and place onto a baking sheet. Bake for 15-20 minutes, until the thickest part of the fish, is just firm.
When done, drizzle with the remaining marinade and serve.

Total Daily Nutritional Facts

Calories: 340	Protein: 36.1g	Total Fat: 19.2g 25%	Trans Fat: 0g
Dietary Fiber: 0.4g 1%	Sugars: 0.3g	Cholesterol: 40mg 15%	Sodium: 307mg 13%
Saturated Fat: 2.1g 11%	Total Carbs: 1.2g 0%		

Vegetable Couscous

Serves
3 Persons

Preparation Time
15 min

Cooking Time
20 min

Ingredients

1 cup couscous
1 ½ cup vegetable stock
3 tbsp tomato paste
3 tbsp lemon juice
1 medium-sized onion, finely chopped
¼ tsp of chili powder
¼ tsp of salt
¼ tsp of black pepper
3 tbsp of olive oil

Preparation

Place couscous in a medium-sized pan and add vegetable stock. Bring it to a boil and reduce the heat to low. Cook for ten minutes, stirring constantly – until the couscous absorbs all the liquid. Remove from the heat and set aside.

Meanwhile, preheat the olive oil in a large skillet. Add onions and stir-fry until translucent. Stir in tomato paste and lemon juice. Season with salt, pepper, and chili powder.

Finally, add couscous and give it a good stir. Cook for 2 more minutes and remove from the heat.

Cool completely before serving.

Total Daily Nutritional Facts

Calories: 372	Protein: 8.8g	Total Fat: 14.7g 19%	Trans Fat: 0g
Dietary Fiber: 4.8g 17%	Sugars: 4.2g	Cholesterol: 0mg 0%	Sodium: 247mg 11%
Saturated Fat: 2.2g 11%	Total Carbs: 52.1g 17%		

Italian Seafood Salad with Red Oranges

Serves
3 Persons

Preparation Time
15 min

Cooking Time
20 min

Ingredients

1 cup fresh lettuce, chopped
1 medium-sized cucumber, sliced
1 red bell pepper, sliced
7 oz frozen seafood mix
1 medium-sized onion, finely chopped
2 garlic cloves, crushed
4 tbsp extra virgin olive oil
½ sea salt

Preparation

Wash and prepare the vegetables. Place in a large serving bowl and set aside.
Heat up 3 tbsp olive oil over medium-high heat. Add onions and garlic and stir-fry for 2-3 minutes. Add seafood and continue to cook for 15 minutes, or until all the liquid evaporates. Remove from the heat and chill to a room temperature.
Transfer the seafood to the serving bowl and combine with vegetables. Drizzle with the remaining oil and season with salt.
Serve immediately.

Total Daily Nutritional Facts

Calories: 267	Protein: 11.1g	Total Fat: 19.6g 25%	Trans Fat: 0g
Dietary Fiber: 2g 7%	Sugars: 5.4g	Cholesterol: 68mg 25%	Sodium: 291mg 13%
Saturated Fat: 3.3g 17%	Total Carbs: 12.8g 4%		

Scrambled Eggs with Cranberries

Serves
2 Persons

Preparation Time
05 min

Cooking Time
02 min

Ingredients

3 large eggs
½ cup fresh goat's cheese
1 tbsp Italian seasoning
2 tbsp extra virgin olive oil
¼ cup fresh cranberries

Preparation

Heat up the oil in a small skillet. Crack the eggs into a small bowl. Use a fork to beat them together. Season with Italian seasoning and pour into the skillet.
Stir slowly with a kitchen spatula and cook for 2 minutes, or until slightly underdone. Remove from the heat and top with cranberries. Serve immediately.

Total Daily Nutritional Facts

Calories: 359	Protein: 15.6g	Total Fat: 32g 41%	Trans Fat: 0g
Dietary Fiber: 0.5g 2%	Sugars: 2.4g	Cholesterol: 306mg 111%	Sodium: 253mg 11%
Saturated Fat: 10.5g 53%	Total Carbs: 3.3g 1%		

Spinach Triangles

6 Persons

Preparation Time
25 min

Cooking Time
20 min

Ingredients

1 cup spinach, chopped
¼ cup goat's cheese
¼ cup skim milk
2 egg whites
1 egg yolk
2 tbsp extra virgin olive oil
¼ tsp salt
2 sheets frozen filo pastry, defrosted

Preparation

Preheat the oven to 400 degrees. Line some parchment paper over a large baking sheet and set aside.
Rinse the spinach thoroughly and drain in a colander. Transfer to a large bowl.
Add goat's cheese, milk, and egg whites. Season with salt and stir well until completely combined.
Cut each pastry sheet into three strips. Place one tablespoon of the spinach mixture on the underside of a strip of pastry.
Fold the tip over the filling to form a triangle, folding the strip in a zigzag manner until the filling is wrapped in a triangle.
Transfer onto the baking sheet and bake for 20 minutes, or until golden brown.

Total Daily Nutritional Facts

Calories: 125	Protein: 4.4g	Total Fat: 7.3g 9%	Trans Fat: 0g
Dietary Fiber: 0.5g 2%	Sugars: 1.1g	Cholesterol: 39mg 14%	Sodium: 143mg 6%
Saturated Fat: 1.9g 10%	Total Carbs: 10.5g 3%,		

Lemon Baked Chicken

Serves
4 Persons

Preparation Time
45 min

Cooking Time
1 hr 30 min

Ingredients

1 three-pound chicken
¼ cup freshly squeezed lemon juice
2 tbsp lemon zest
1 tbsp honey
1 tbsp dried rosemary
½ tsp salt

Preparation

Thoroughly rinse the chicken and pat dry with a kitchen paper. Set aside.
Whisk together lemon juice, zest, honey, and rosemary. Loosen the skin of the chicken from the flesh.
Rub this mixture under the skin and place in a large plastic bag. Refrigerate for 30 minutes.
Preheat the oven to 350 degrees. Line some parchment paper over a medium-sized baking dish and set aside. Remove the chicken from the refrigerator and brush with the remaining lemon mixture.
Bake for 1 hour and 30 minutes.

Total Daily Nutritional Facts

Calories: 347

Protein: 49.5g

Total Fat: 12.9g 17%

Trans Fat: 0g

Dietary Fiber: 0.6g 2%

Sugars: 4.8g

Cholesterol: 151mg 55%

Sodium: 441mg 19%

Saturated Fat: 3.7g 18%

Total Carbs: 5.8g 2%

Braised Greens with Rice

Serves
4 Persons

Preparation Time
5 min

Cooking Time
30 min

Ingredients

4 oz kale, chopped
4 oz spinach, chopped
4 oz collard greens, chopped
2 oz Swiss chard, chopped
1 medium-sized leek, chopped
1 cup brown rice
3 tbsp olive oil
1 tsp sea salt

Preparation

Wash all greens thoroughly under cold running water and drain in a large colander. Using a sharp knife, chop the vegetables and set aside.

Place rice in a deep pot and pour in three cups of water. Bring it to a boil and reduce the heat to low. Simmer for 15 minutes, or until all the water evaporates. Stir occasionally. Remove from the heat and set aside.

Meanwhile, place the greens in a large pot. Pour in enough water to cover and briefly cook, for 2-3 minutes. Remove from the heat and drain. Grease a large skillet with olive oil. Add greens and cook for 5-7 minutes, stirring constantly. Stir in the rice and cook for 2 more minutes. Remove from the heat and serve.

Optionally, drizzle with freshly squeezed lemon or lime juice.

Total Daily Nutritional Facts

Calories: 303	Protein: 6.2g	Total Fat: 11.2g 14%	Trans Fat: 0g
Dietary Fiber: 3.2g 12%	Sugars: 1.2g	Cholesterol: 0mg 0%	Sodium: 544mg 24%
Saturated Fat: 21.6g 8%	Total Carbs: 46.2g 15%		

Vanilla Pancakes

Serves
6 Persons

Preparation Time
7 min

Cooking Time
3 min

Ingredients

2 medium-sized bananas, mashed
1 ¼ cup goat's milk
2 eggs
1 ½ cup rolled oats
1 ½ tsp baking powder
1 tsp vanilla extract
2 tsp coconut oil
1 tbsp honey
¼ tsp salt
Non-fat cooking spray

Preparation

Combine the ingredients in a blender and pulse until completely smooth batter. Set aside.
Heat griddle or a large, non-stick skillet to medium-high heat. Spray with cooking spray. Add ¼ cup of the batter and cook until firm and golden brown, for 2 minutes. Carefully flip and cook for one more minute. *Serve immediately.*

Total Daily Nutritional Facts

Calories: 190	Protein: 6.7g	Total Fat: 5.9g 8%	Trans Fat: 0g
Dietary Fiber: 3.1g 11%	Sugars: 10.4g	Cholesterol: 67mg 24%	Sodium: 144mg 6%
Saturated Fat: 2.9g 14%	Total Carbs: 28.8g 10%		

Collard Greens with Veal

Serves	Preparation Time	Cooking Time
4 Persons	**20** min	**1 hr 20 min**

Ingredients

1 lb veal brisket, cut into half-inch thick pieces
3 celery stalks, sliced
1 large carrot, sliced
1 bay leaf
1 tsp sea salt
½ tsp freshly ground black pepper
2 lbs collard greens
¼ cup brown rice
3 garlic cloves, crushed
¼ cup olive oil
½ lemon, juiced

Preparation

Rinse the meat and pat dry with a kitchen towel. Place in a pressure cooker along with celery stalks, carrot, bay leaf, salt, and pepper. Pour in enough water to cover and seal the lid. Cook for 45 minutes, or until completely tender.

Release the cooker's pressure and open the lid. Remove the meat but reserve the broth. Set aside.

Place rice in a medium-sized pan and pour in 1 cup of broth. Bring it to a boil and reduce the heat to medium-low. Simmer for 12-15 minutes, stirring constantly. When done, remove from the heat and set aside.

Finally, rinse the collard greens under cold running water and drain in a large colander. Using a sharp cutting knife, roughly chop the greens and place in a large pot. Pour in enough water to cover and bring it to a boil. Cook for 3 minutes. Remove from the heat and drain.

Preheat two tablespoons of olive oil in a large skillet. Add garlic and stir-fry for 2-3 minutes. Now add the meat and briefly brown, on both sides. Stir in greens and rice and mix well. Cook for 3-4 minutes, stirring constantly.

Remove from the heat and drizzle with the remaining olive oil and lemon juice. *Serve immediately!*

Total Daily Nutritional Facts

Calories: 423	Protein: 33.9g	Saturated Fat: 5.3g 26%	Total Fat: 22.9g 29%
Total Carbs: 25.6g 9%	Trans Fat: 0g	Cholesterol: 117mg 43%	Sodium: 624mg 27%
Dietary Fiber: 8.6g 31%	Sugars: 1.3g		

Tender Octopus Salad

Serves
6 Persons

Preparation Time
5-10 min

Cooking Time
10 min

Ingredients

2 lbs fresh octopus
3 large onions, finely chopped
3 tbsp extra virgin olive oil
2 garlic cloves, crushed
1 tsp dried rosemary
1 tbsp fresh parsley leaves, finely chopped
¼ cup capers
¼ cup olives
½ tsp sea salt
¼ tsp freshly ground black pepper

Preparation

Place octopus in your pressure cooker and pour in enough water to cover. Seal the lid and cook for 1 hour, or until completely tender. Release the pressure and remove the octopus. Chill for a while and cut into bite-sized pieces. Set aside.

Heat up the olive oil over medium-high heat. Add onions, garlic, and rosemary. Stir-fry for 3-4 minutes. Stir in chopped octopus, capers, and parsley. Season with salt and pepper and cook for one minute. Remove from the heat and cool completely. Add olives and serve.

Optionally, drizzle with freshly squeezed lemon juice.

Total Daily Nutritional Facts

Calories: 349	Protein: 45.6g	Total Fat: 11.3g 15%	Trans Fat: 0g
Dietary Fiber: 2.1g 8%	Sugars: 3.2g	Cholesterol: 142mg 52%	Sodium: 1072mg 47%
Saturated Fat: 1.1g 6%	Total Carbs: 15.3g 5%		

Mushroom Omelet

Serves
3 Persons

Preparation Time
15 min

Cooking Time
15 min

Ingredients

3 eggs
½ cup fresh goat's cheese
¼ cup milk
1 cup button mushrooms
1 large onion, finely chopped
1 tsp dried oregano
¼ tsp sea salt
2 tbsp olive oil

Preparation

In a medium-sized skillet, heat up the olive oil over medium-high heat. Add onions and stir-fry until translucent. Season with oregano and add button mushrooms. Continue to cook for 5-7 minutes over medium-low heat. Stir occasionally.

Crack the eggs into a mixing bowl and season with oregano. Add goat's cheese and milk. Whisk together and set aside.

Remove the mushrooms from the skillet and set aside. Pour the egg mixture into the skillet and cook for 2 minutes, stirring constantly.

Serve with button mushrooms.

Total Daily Nutritional Facts

Calories: 248	Protein: 11.6g	Total Fat: 19.9g 26%	Trans Fat: 0g
Dietary Fiber: 1.5g 5%	Sugars: 4.3g	Cholesterol: 180mg 66%	Sodium: 328mg 14%
Saturated Fat: 6.8g 34%	Total Carbs: 7.6g 3%		

Vegetable Paella

Serves
6 Persons

Preparation Time
15 min

Cooking Time
20-25 min

Ingredients

½ cup green peas
2 small carrots, finely chopped
1 cup fire-roasted tomatoes
1 cup zucchini, finely chopped
½ cup celery root, finely chopped
8 saffron threads
1 tbsp turmeric, ground
1 tsp salt
½ tsp freshly ground black pepper
2 cup vegetable stock
1 cup long grain rice

Preparation

Combine rice, green peas, carrots, and celery root in a deep, heavy-bottomed pot. Pour in vegetable stock and two cups of water. Stir well and bring it to a boil. Reduce the heat to medium-low and cook for 10-12 minutes, stirring occasionally.

Now stir in zucchini, fire-roasted tomatoes, saffron threads, turmeric, salt, and pepper. Mix well and pour in about one cup of water. Continue to cook for 6-7 minutes, stirring constantly.

Remove from the heat and serve.

Total Daily Nutritional Facts

Calories: 164	Protein: 4.4g	Total Fat: 1g 1%	Trans Fat: 0g
Dietary Fiber: 3.3g 12%	Sugars: 4.3g	Cholesterol: 0mg 0%	Sodium: 560mg 24%
Saturated Fat: 0.1g 1%	Total Carbs: 34.5g 11%		

Strawberry Vanilla Rolls

Serves	Preparation Time	Cooking Time
4 Persons	**20** min	**15-20** min

Ingredients

2 cups fresh strawberries, chopped
2 puff pastry sheets
2 tbsp cornstarch
3 oz vanilla pudding powder
5 cups skim milk
6 tbsp powdered stevia, plus 2 tbsp
1 large egg
1 tsp strawberry
extract, sugar-free

Preparation

Preheat the oven to 400 degrees.
Wash the strawberries under cold running water. Remove stems and place it in a food processor. Blend until pureed and set aside.
In a medium-sized saucepan, combine strawberries, cornstarch, 2 tablespoons of stevia, and strawberry extract. Add 2 tablespoons of water bring it to a boil. Give it a good stir and remove from the heat.
Combine milk and the remaining stevia in a heavy-bottomed pot over a medium-high heat. Bring it to a boil and then stir in the vanilla pudding powder. Reduce the heat to low and cook about 3-4 minutes, stirring constantly. Remove from the heat and cool completely.
In a separate bowl, lightly beat the egg and set aside.
Unfold the pastry and cut each sheet into 4-inch x 7-inch pieces and brush with egg mixture. Now, add 2 tablespoons of strawberry mixture and then 2 tablespoons of pudding in the middle of each sheet. Fold the sheets and brush with the remaining egg mixture.
Transfer to a baking sheet and bake for 15-20 minutes or until puffed and golden brown.

Total Daily Nutritional Facts

Calories: 360	Protein: 13.6g	Cholesterol: 70mg 25%	Sugars: 17.1g
Dietary Fiber: 2g 7%	Trans Fat: 0g	Sodium: 480mg 21%	Total Carbs: 54.1g 18%
Saturated Fat: 4.9g 11%	Total Fat: 9g 11%		

Sweet Potato and Pumpkin Soup

Serves	Preparation Time	Cooking Time
4 Persons	**15** min	**60** min

Ingredients

2 lbs pumpkin, peeled and cut into chunks
3 large carrots, sliced
3 medium-sized sweet potatoes
2 celery stalks, chopped
4 cups vegetable broth
¼ cup heavy cream
2 tbsp olive oil
½ tsp salt
¼ tsp freshly ground black pepper

Preparation

Preheat the oven to 400 degrees. Line some parchment paper over a baking sheet.

Peel and cut the pumpkin into chunks. Place onto a baking sheet and roast for 35-40 minutes. Remove from the oven and chill for a while.

Grease a deep pan with olive oil and heat up over medium-high heat. Add carrots and celery. Stir-fry for 3-4 minutes, shaking the pan regularly.

Add roasted pumpkin and sweet potatoes. Pour in the vegetable broth and season with salt and pepper. Bring it to a boil and reduce the heat to medium-low.

Cook for 15 minutes, stirring occasionally.

Remove the soup from the heat and cool to a room temperature.

Transfer to a blender or a food processor and pulse until smooth. *Serve warm.*

Total Daily Nutritional Facts

Calories: 300	Protein: 9.5g	Total Fat: 11.8g 15%	Trans Fat: 0g
Dietary Fiber: 11.1g 40%	Sugars: 16.2g	Cholesterol: 10mg 4%	Sodium: 1165mg 51%
Saturated Fat: 3.4g 17%	Total Carbs: 42.4g 14%		

Overnight Oats with Fruits

Serves
2 Persons

Preparation Time
10 min

Ingredients

½ cup rolled oats
1 cup skim milk
½ cup plain yogurt
½ cup blueberries
¼ cup strawberries
1 tsp blueberry extract
1 tbsp honey

Preparation

Combine milk, yogurt, blueberries, strawberries, blueberry extract, and honey in a blender. Pulse until completely smooth.
Stir in oats and refrigerate overnight.

Total Daily Nutritional Facts

Calories: 241	Protein: 10.6g	Total Fat: 4.8g 6%	Trans Fat: 0g
Dietary Fiber: 3.3g 12%	Sugars: 23.1g	Cholesterol: 14mg 5%	Sodium: 102mg 4%
Saturated Fat: 2.3g 12%	Total Carbs: 39.4g 13%		

Spanish Paella

Serves
4 Persons

Preparation Time
15 min

Cooking Time
20 min

Ingredients

1 cup rice
7 oz frozen seafood mix, defrosted
1 large onion, finely chopped
1 large tomato, finely chopped
¼ cup green peas
1 tsp turmeric powder
2 tbsp olive oil
2 garlic cloves, crushed
1 tbsp fresh rosemary
½ tsp sea salt

Preparation

Place rice in a deep pot and pour in three tablespoons of water.
Bring it to a boil and stir in turmeric powder.
Reduce the heat to medium-low and cook for 10-12 minutes, stirring occasionally.
Remove from the heat and set aside.
Meanwhile, heat up the olive oil over medium-high heat. Add finely chopped onion and garlic. Stir-fry for one minute.
Now add seafood and season with salt and rosemary. Cook for 15 minutes, stirring occasionally.
Finally, stir in rice and mix well. Cook for another 2 minutes and remove from the heat.
Optionally, sprinkle with grated Parmesan cheese.

Total Daily Nutritional Facts

Calories: 316	Protein: 12.8g	Total Fat: 8.2g 10%	Trans Fat: 0g
Dietary Fiber: 2.9g 10%	Sugars: 3.4g	Cholesterol: 58mg 21%	Sodium: 416mg 18%
Saturated Fat: 1.7g 8%	Total Carbs: 46.2g 15%		

Lemon Stuffed Tench

Serves
3 Persons

Preparation Time
15 min

Cooking Time
8 min

Ingredients

1 medium-sized tench, cleaned and gutted
1 whole lemon, sliced
2 tbsp extra virgin olive oil
1 tsp fresh rosemary, finely chopped
¼ tsp dried thyme, ground
2 garlic cloves, crushed
½ tsp sea salt

Preparation

Preheat the grill to high heat.
Rinse the fish thoroughly under cold running water. Pat dry using a kitchen paper. Set aside.
In a small bowl, combine olive oil, rosemary, thyme, garlic, and salt. Stir until combined. Generously brush the fish with
previously prepared mixture and stuff with lemon slices.
Grill for 3-4 minutes on each side.

Total Daily Nutritional Facts

Calories: 249	Protein: 24.4g	Total Fat: 15.5g 20%	Trans Fat: 0g
Dietary Fiber: 0.8g 3%	Sugars: 0.5g	Cholesterol: 0mg 0%	Sodium: 313mg 14%
Saturated Fat: 1.4g 7%	Total Carbs: 2.8g 1%		

Recipes in this Cookbook - Overview

By now I hope you have realized that the Mediterranean diet is not complicated nor something to be afraid of. This book was designed to help you eat clean, tasty food, prepared in the healthiest way possible – the Mediterranean way, made with pure organic ingredients that are bursting with flavors and different nutrients. When combined with specific herbs and spices and the irreplaceable olive oil, these recipes provide new health benefits and flavors. These 147 recipes are based on fresh, organic ingredients that are especially good for weight loss and overall health. And to make things even easier in your weight loss journey, I have created a beautifully delicious meal plan along with shopping lists for you to follow. With this book as your guide, losing weight will never be easier.

Make sure to try all the recipes and leave some comments. Your feedback and comments mean the world to me. Please take a moment and tell me what you think about these meals and preparation methods. Both positive and negative feedback are welcome.

Thank you for taking the time to go through this cookbook and enjoy your new Mediterranean lifestyle!

Wish you all the best,

Matthew A. Bryant